GCSE
English Language
Reading: Non-Fiction

Analysing non-fiction is one of the toughest parts of the AQA GCSE English Language exam. It takes lots of practice — and that's where this book comes in.

It's full of superb non-fiction texts with exam-style questions, plus a realistic reading practice paper to put your skills to the test. With this book, you'll be fully equipped to get a top mark in the Reading section of the AQA Paper 2 exam.

And of course, we've included clear, in-depth answers at the back of the book. When it comes to strengthening your non-fiction analysis, this book is the bee's knees!

CGP — still the best! ☺

Our sole aim here at CGP is to produce the highest quality books — carefully written, immaculately presented and dangerously close to being funny.

Then we work our socks off to get them out to you
— at the cheapest possible prices.

Exam Practice Workbook
For Paper 2

Published by CGP

Editors:
Keith Blackhall, Siân Butler, Tom Carney, Rachel Craig-McFeely, Emma Duffee, Sean Walsh

With thanks to Andy Cashmore for the proofreading.
With thanks to Laura Jakubowski for the copyright research.

Acknowledgements:

We would like to thank the following copyright holders:

'Down Under' by Bill Bryson. Published by Doubleday.
Reprinted by permission of The Random House Group Limited. © 2000

'Letters from Australia' are available online on QueenSpark Books' Letter in the Attic project.

'Secret Teacher: teaching in prisons is where I can make a real difference' by anon.
Copyright Guardian News & Media Ltd 2018

'He Knows the Score' by Edward Seckerson first published in 1996 by Independent.
Reproduced with permission from Independent Digital News & Media Ltd.

'Smoke on the water: a boating holiday adventure in France' by Emma Cook. Copyright Guardian News & Media Ltd 2018

'The Story of Hooverville in Seattle' by Jesse Jackson is from Real Change News. Used by permission

'The Exmoor Files' by Liz Jones. The Orion Publishing Group, London. © Liz Jones 2009.

'How to keep to a budget while at uni' is from The Good Universities Guide, www.gooduniversitiesguide.com.au

'Londoners: The Days and Nights of London Now - as Told by Those Who Love it, Hate it, Live it, Left it and Long for it' by Craig Taylor. Published by Granta Books.

'Read this before you go sales shopping: the environmental costs of fast fashion' by Patsy Perry, Senior Lecturer in Fashion Marketing, The University of Manchester. First published on The Conversation (theconversation.com/uk) and licenced under Attribution-NoDerivatives 4.0 International (CC BY-ND 4.0) creativecommons.org/licenses/by-nd/4.0/

'Wildest dreams: a family camping trip in Oman' by Fiona McAuslan. Copyright Guardian News & Media Ltd 2018

'Acting French' by Ta-Nehisi Coates. © 2014 The Atlantic Media Co., as first published in TheAtlantic.com.
All rights reserved. Distributed by Tribune Content Agency.

Extract on pg 75-76 'My apple's not perfect, but this art class has appeal' by Harry Mount © dmg media licensing

The extracts in this book have been carefully selected to develop GCSE students' English Language skills.
CGP accepts no further responsibility for the content of published works by their authors.

This book contains exam style questions — these are not official AQA questions and this book is not endorsed by AQA.

ISBN: 978 1 78908 006 3
Printed by Elanders Ltd, Newcastle upon Tyne.

Based on the classic CGP style created by Richard Parsons.

Exam Structure

You'll sit <u>two</u> papers, each worth <u>50%</u> of your GCSE. This book covers reading skills for <u>Paper 2</u>.

You will sit two different papers

1) Each English Language paper lasts <u>1 hour 45 minutes</u> and is worth <u>80 marks</u>.

2) Paper 1 focuses on <u>fiction</u>. You'll be given <u>one</u> literary fiction extract from either the <u>20th</u> or <u>21st century</u>.

> <u>Section A</u> assesses <u>reading</u>. It has <u>four</u> questions based on the literary fiction extract.
>
> <u>Section B</u> assesses <u>writing</u>. You'll need to respond to <u>one</u> fiction writing prompt from a <u>choice of two</u>.

3) Paper 2 focuses on <u>non-fiction</u>. You'll be given <u>two</u> non-fiction extracts —
   one from the <u>19th century</u>, and one from either the <u>20th</u> or <u>21st century</u>.

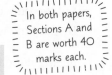
In both papers, Sections A and B are worth 40 marks each.

> <u>Section A</u> assesses <u>reading</u>. It has <u>four</u> questions based on the two <u>non-fiction extracts</u>.
>
> <u>Section B</u> assesses <u>writing</u>. You'll need to respond to one <u>non-fiction writing prompt</u>.

This book tests your non-fiction reading skills

1) All the questions in this book focus on the skills which are needed for <u>Section A</u> of <u>Paper 2</u>.

2) Section A of Paper 2 assesses <u>three</u> of the <u>assessment objectives (AOs)</u>:

AO1	• Find <u>explicit</u> and <u>implicit</u> information, and <u>put together</u> information from different texts.
AO2	• <u>Explain</u> how writers use <u>language</u> and <u>structure</u> to achieve a <u>purpose</u> or <u>influence</u> readers. • Use <u>technical terms</u> to support your analysis.
AO3	• Compare writers' <u>ideas</u>, <u>perspectives</u>, and the <u>methods</u> they use.

In total, there are six AOs which are tested across the two papers.

3) There are <u>four</u> questions in Section A — make sure you familiarise yourself with each of them:

> • <u>Question 1</u> tests <u>AO1</u> and is worth <u>four</u> marks. It focuses on <u>specific</u> lines from <u>one</u> extract.
> • You'll be given <u>eight</u> statements — you need to identify which <u>four</u> statements are <u>true</u>.
> • Some statements require you to make <u>inferences</u> about things that <u>aren't</u> explicitly stated.

> • <u>Question 2</u> also tests <u>AO1</u> and is worth <u>eight</u> marks. It focuses on the <u>whole</u> of <u>both</u> extracts.
> • You'll have to <u>summarise</u> the <u>similarities</u> or <u>differences</u> between a shared idea in both texts.
> • You should make <u>inferences</u> about the extracts and give a range of <u>examples</u>.

> • <u>Question 3</u> tests <u>AO2</u> and is worth <u>twelve</u> marks. It focuses on <u>specific</u> lines from <u>one</u> extract.
> • You'll need to analyse how <u>language</u> is used to achieve <u>effects</u> and <u>influence</u> the reader.
> • Your answer should use a range of <u>examples</u> and relevant <u>subject terminology</u>.

> • <u>Question 4</u> tests <u>AO3</u> and is worth <u>sixteen</u> marks. It focuses on the <u>whole</u> of <u>both</u> extracts.
> • You'll have to <u>compare</u> how the two writers convey their similar or different <u>perspectives</u>.
> • Your answer should compare the writers' <u>ideas</u> as well as analysing <u>how</u> they express them.

Section One — Australian Adventures

Exercise A — Down Under

Extract A — From 'Down Under: Travels in a Sunburned Country' by Bill Bryson, 2000

Bill Bryson is a popular author who has written books about science, language and history. He is perhaps best known for his travel writing, which is usually as entertaining as it is informative.

Even now, the emptiness of so much of Australia is startling. The landscape we passed through was officially only 'semi-desert', but it was as barren an expanse as I had ever seen. Every twenty or twenty-five kilometres there would be a dirt track and a lonely mailbox signalling an unseen sheep or cattle station*. Once a light truck flew past in a bouncing hell-for-leather fashion, spraying us with gravelly dinks and a coating of red dust,
5   but the only other lively thing was the endless shaking flubbity-dubbing of the axles over the corduroy road*. By the time we reached White Cliffs, in mid-afternoon, we felt as if we had spent the day in a cement mixer.

Seeing it today, it is all but impossible to believe that White Cliffs, a small blotch of habitations under a hard clear sky, was once a boom town, with a population of nearly 4,500, a hospital, a newspaper, a library and a busy core of general stores, hotels, restaurants, brothels and gaming houses. Today central White Cliffs consists
10   of a pub, a launderette, an opal shop, and a grocery/café/petrol station. The permanent population is about eighty. They exist in a listless world of heat and dust. If you were looking for people with the tolerance and fortitude to colonize Mars this would be the place to come.

Because of the heat, most houses in town are burrowed into the faces of the two bleached hills from which the town takes its name. The most ambitious of these dwellings, and the principal magnet for the relatively few
15   tourists who venture this far, is the Dug-Out Underground Motel, a twenty-six-room complex cut deep into the rocks on the side of Smith's Hill. Wandering through its network of rocky tunnels was like stepping into an early James Bond movie, in one of those subterranean* complexes where the loyal minions of SMERSH* are preparing to take over the world by melting Antarctica or hijacking the White House with the aid of a giant magnet. The attraction of burrowing into the hillside is immediately evident when you step inside - a constant
20   year-round temperature of 67 degrees. The rooms were very nice and quite normal except that the walls and ceilings were cavelike and windowless. When the lights were off, the darkness and silence were total.

I don't know how much money you would have to give me to persuade me to settle in White Cliffs – something in the low zillions, I suppose – but that evening as we sat on the motel's lofty garden terrace with Leon Hornby, the proprietor, drinking beer and watching the evening slink in, I realized that my fee might be marginally
25   negotiable. I was about to ask Leon – a city man by birth and, I would have guessed, inclination – what possessed him and his pleasant wife Marge to stay in this godforsaken outpost where even a run to the supermarket means a six-hour round-trip over a rutted dirt road, but before I could speak a remarkable thing happened. Kangaroos hopped into the expansive foreground and began grazing picturesquely, and the sun plonked onto the horizon, like a stage prop lowered on a wire, and the towering western skies before us spread
30   with colour in a hundred layered shades – glowing pinks, deep purples, careless banners of pure crimson – all on a scale that you cannot imagine, for there was not a scrap of intrusion in the forty miles of visible desert that lay between us and the far horizon. It was the most extraordinarily vivid sunset I believe I have ever seen.

'I came up here thirty years ago to build reservoirs on the
35   sheep stations,' Leon said, as if anticipating my question, 'and never expected to stay, but somehow the place gets to you. I'd find these sunsets hard to give up, for one thing.'

Glossary:
sheep or cattle station — a large animal-specific farm
corduroy road — a road made out of tree trunks
subterranean — underground
SMERSH — a fictional enemy organisation from the James Bond novels

Exercise C — Comparing Texts

Q1 Both texts are written to entertain. Compare the methods each writer uses to achieve this.

....

....

....

....

....

....

....

....

....

Q2 Compare how the writers convey their different attitudes to travelling by boat.

PAPER 2
Q4

In your answer, you could:
• compare their different attitudes
• compare the methods the writers use to convey their different attitudes
• support your response with references to both texts.

Make a plan in the space below, then write your answer on a separate piece of paper.

Extension Activity

RESEARCH TASK

Look for other examples of travel or holiday-themed texts that are about different modes of transport (for example, cars, aeroplanes, trains, animals, hot air balloons or even walking). Think about how the language that's used to describe the journey changes for each mode of transport.

Exercise A — The Story of Hooverville in Seattle

Extract A — Abridged from 'The Story of Hooverville in Seattle' by Jesse Jackson, 1935

When the American stock market crashed in 1929, it caused a huge economic crisis called the 'Great Depression'. It led to millions of people losing their jobs and homes. All over America, the homeless built camps which were known as 'Hoovervilles', named after the president at the time, Herbert Hoover. Jesse Jackson became known as the unofficial 'mayor' of Seattle's 'Hooverville'.

This is a true story of my own experiences. I was one of the first 20 to build a shack upon the property of the Seattle Port Commission located upon Seattle's waterfront that was destined to pass through many difficulties, and grow to a little shanty city* of 600 shacks and 1,000 inhabitants.

5 I was registered at a Central Registry for single homeless men and given a ticket that called for one evening meal at a soup kitchen that resembled pig swill more than it did human food; no morning or noonday meal; and was allowed to sleep upon the hard floor of the institution at night with a few newspapers that I had picked up, under me for a bed. No beds or bedding had as yet been provided. These conditions caused me to rebel against the relief setup and start to find a way to get away from the whole thing. I walked down the waterfront to the vacant property of the Seattle Port Commission where a shipyard once was located. When the

10 shipyard moved to another location, it left behind concrete machinery pits plenty big enough to make a room, and plenty of scrap lumber* and tin that could be used to build crude* shelters, any of which would be a big improvement over the hard floors of the charitable institution. The day I went down the street to this property, there were a dozen others who were of the same mind as I. We were among the first to face and taste the bitter realities of a system that would not provide employment for willing workers to enable them to care for

15 themselves or provide a humane system to relieve their suffering in such a time as this.

We immediately set in, with the resources we found strewn over this vacant property, to construct and work out a relief system of our own. It was not many days before our numbers increased, and within 30 days the shanty town had grown to near 100 shacks, and then we faced our first difficulty.

The Seattle health officials decided our shacks were unfit for human habitation and posted official notices on

20 our doors notifying us of the fact and giving us seven days in which to vacate. We had no other places to go and thought that the authorities were bluffing, so we paid no attention to the notices. The authorities were not bluffing: At the expiration of the seven days notice, at 5 a.m., just as daylight was breaking, in one of the heaviest downpours of rain that fell in Seattle that fall, a regiment of uniformed officers of law and order swooped down upon us with cans of kerosene* and applied the torch. Amidst the confusion that followed,

25 we salvaged our few belongings and, just as soon as the officers were out of sight, we returned and rebuilt our burned shanties. A month later this performance was repeated. This time we did not rebuild, but dug in, indeed. With any kind of digging tool we could find, we shoveled the loose sand out of the concrete pits, over the top of which we placed tin for a roof. This time we knew that there would be no burn-out.

In June 1932 a committee of different city departments visited us. The spokesman told us that we were going to

30 be tolerated until conditions improved, but that they were going to lay down a few simple rules for us.

As several of us sat around an open camp fire one evening, one of the shanty dwellers remarked that "we must have a name for this place; we can't call it any old thing." One man spoke up with "This is the era of Hoover prosperity; let's call this place Hooverville." So the name given through sarcasm to the then

35 President Hoover, has clung to this place ever since.

> Glossary:
> shanty city — an area made up of basic shacks which are home to poor people
> lumber — pieces of wood
> crude — rough or simple
> kerosene — a kind of fuel

Q1   The extract is an account of Jesse Jackson's experiences.

a)   What do you think the purpose of the extract is? Why do you think this?

....

....

....

b)   Jackson tells us that this is a "true story" about his "own experiences".
     How does this aid the purpose of the text?

....

....

....

Q2   Read the second and third paragraphs of the extract.

a)   List three things that you are told about the Central Registry in this part of the extract.

1.   ....

2.   ....

3.   ....

b)   How does Jackson use language to show how he felt about his treatment at the Central Registry?

....

....

....

....

c)   What does Jackson imply about how his time living and working with the other homeless
     people compared to his time at the Central Registry? Explain how he does this.

....

....

....

....

Section Five — Homelessness in History

During the Great Depression, many Americans felt that those in power had failed them. Authorities were instructed to use local taxes to organise relief schemes for those affected by the crisis. However, huge levels of unemployment meant that taxes weren't being paid — so relief schemes were cut and people were left without food or accommodation.

Q3 How would you describe the tone of the extract? How does Jackson convey this?

....

....

....

....

Q4 How is the text structured to interest the reader?

....

....

....

....

....

....

Q5 You now need to refer only to lines 19-28.
How does the writer use language to describe the attempted evictions?

PAPER 2 Q3

Jot down some ideas in the box below, then write your answer on a separate piece of paper.

Make sure you consider the effect on the reader...

When you read an extract, make sure you pay attention to how the writer has created its tone and style. While you're doing that, remember to think about the effect these features have on the reader too.

Exercise B — London Labour and the London Poor

Extract B — Adapted from 'London Labour and the London Poor' by Henry Mayhew, 1851

The poorest in Victorian society lived in workhouses, where they would do awful jobs to earn their keep. Here, Henry Mayhew (an influential Victorian social researcher) offers an insight into the casual wards — the areas of the workhouses which gave homeless people a bed for the night.

I now come to the characteristics of vagrant* life, as seen in the casual wards of the metropolitan unions*. The subject is one of the most important with which I have dealt, and the facts I have collected are sufficiently startling, for they show that the young vagrant is the budding criminal.

5   Before I embarked upon my inquiry into this subject, I consulted with a gentleman who had long paid considerable attention to the question, and who had the greatest experience and the correctest notions upon the matter. He had filled the office of master of the Wandsworth and Clapham Union* for three years, and he has long given much attention to the habits of the vagrants that have come under his notice or care. He told me that he considered a casual ward necessary in every union, because there is always a migratory population, with youths forming more than one-half of it, their ages from twelve to twenty. The largest

10   number were seventeen years old — just that age when youth becomes free from parental control. These lads had generally run away and many had been reared to a life of vagrancy. They were mostly shrewd* and acute youths; some had been very well educated. To use the gentleman's own words, they are certainly not ignorant; indeed, with a few exceptions, he would say they are the reverse.

These lads possess an aversion to continuous labour of any kind. He never knew them to work — they are,

15   indeed, essentially the idle and the vagabond. Their great inclination is to be on the move, and wandering from place to place; and they appear, he says, to receive a great deal of pleasure from the casual ward. They are physically stout, healthy lads, and certainly not emaciated* or sickly. Indeed, they are full of health and mischief. When in London, they occupy themselves by holding horses, and carrying parcels from the docks and railway stations. Some loiter about the markets in the hope of a job, and others may be seen in

20   the streets picking up bones and rags, or along the water-side searching for pieces of old metal, or anything that may be sold at the marine-store shops. They have nearly all been in prison more than once, and several a greater number of times than they are years old. They are the most dishonest of all thieves. He tells me he has frequently known them to rob one another. They are very stubborn and self-willed. They are a most difficult class to govern and they find great delight in thwarting the authorities of the workhouse. They often

25   come down to the casual wards in large bodies of twenty or thirty, with sticks hidden down the legs of their trousers, and with these they rob and beat those who do not belong to their own gang.

In the winter of 1846, the guardians of Wandsworth and Clapham, sympathising with the vagrants' ragged and wretched appearance, and hoping to offer them the means of obtaining an honest livelihood, gave my informant instructions to give refuge to any who might choose

30   to remain in the workhouse. Under this arrangement, about fifty were admitted. The majority were under seventeen years of age. Some of them remained a few days — others a few weeks — none stopped longer than three months. The restrictions and order of the workhouse were especially irksome* to them. This is the character

35   of the true vagrant, for whom my informant considers no provision whatsoever should be made.

Glossary:
vagrant — a homeless person
unions — groups of parishes
Wandsworth and Clapham Union —
a union in south-west London
shrewd — able to quickly judge a situation
emaciated — extremely thin
irksome — irritating

Q1   How has the first paragraph been written to appeal to you as a reader?

....

....

....

In 1834, a Poor Law was introduced which made local unions responsible for establishing and running workhouses. Although they offered aid to the poor, conditions were awful — there were harsh rules to follow and residents had to carry out back-breaking labour. This was supposed to deter people from turning to the workhouses unless it was absolutely necessary.

Q2   Who do you think the intended audience of the extract is? Why do you think this?

....

....

....

....

Q3   You now need to refer only to lines 14-26.
How does the writer use language to describe the young people?

PAPER 2
Q3

Write down some thoughts in the box below, then write your answer on a separate piece of paper.

A writer's experiences often influence their work...

It's useful to consider a writer's perspective when you read an extract — think about how they approach the issue, whether it has affected their writing or if they have considered both sides of the argument.

Exercise C — Comparing Texts

Q1   Do you think that Jesse Jackson and Henry Mayhew have similar views about those in power? Explain your answer.

....

....

....

....

....

....

....

....

....

....

Q2   The extracts present homeless people differently. Use details from both extracts to write a summary of the different representations of homeless people.

PAPER 2
Q2

Make some notes in the box, then write your answer on a separate piece of paper.

Extension Activity

Both writers wrote about homelessness because, much like today, it was an important issue in society. Try to think of other examples (fiction or non-fiction) where current events have inspired writing. Why do you think writers reference social issues? What are they trying to achieve?

RESEARCH TASK

Section Five — Homelessness in History

Exercise A — A Lady's Life in the Rocky Mountains

Extract A — Abridged from 'A Lady's Life in the Rocky Mountains' by Isabella L. Bird, 1879

Isabella Bird was an English explorer and writer. She visited lots of places, from Australia and China, to America and Hawaii. In 1873, she rode over 800 miles through the Rocky Mountains.

I have found a dream of beauty at which one might look all one's life and sigh. Not lovable, like the Sandwich Islands*, but beautiful in its own way! A strictly North American beauty — snow-splotched mountains, huge pines, red-woods, sugar pines, silver spruce; a crystalline atmosphere, waves of the richest color; and a pine-hung lake which mirrors all beauty on its surface. Lake Tahoe is before me,

5   a sheet of water twenty-two miles long by ten broad, and in some places 1,700 feet deep. It lies at a height of 6,000 feet, and the snow-crowned summits which wall it in are from 8,000 to 11,000 feet in altitude. The air is keen and elastic. There is no sound but the distant and slightly musical ring of the lumberer's axe.

It is a weariness to go back, even in thought, to the clang of San Francisco, which I left in its cold

10   morning fog early yesterday, driving to the Oakland ferry through streets with side-walks heaped with thousands of cantaloupe* and water-melons, tomatoes, cucumbers, squashes, pears, grapes, peaches, apricots — all of startling size as compared with any I ever saw before. Other streets were piled with sacks of flour, left out all night, owing to the security from rain at this season. I pass hastily over the early part of the journey, the crossing the bay in a fog as chill as November, the number of "lunch

15   baskets," which gave the car the look of conveying a great picnic party, the last view of the Pacific, on which I had looked for nearly a year, the fierce sunshine and brilliant sky inland, the look of long RAINLESSNESS, which one may not call drought, the valleys with sides crimson with the poison oak, the dusty vineyards, with great purple clusters thick among the leaves, and between the vines great dusty melons lying on the dusty earth. From off the boundless harvest fields the grain was carried in

20   June, and it is now stacked in sacks along the track, awaiting freightage*. The barns are bursting with fullness. In the dusty orchards the apple and pear branches are supported, that they may not break down under the weight of fruit; melons, tomatoes, and squashes of gigantic size lie almost unheeded on the ground; fat cattle, gorged almost to repletion, shade themselves under the oaks; superb "red" horses shine, not with grooming, but with condition; and thriving farms everywhere show on what

25   a solid basis the prosperity of the "Golden State" is founded. Very uninviting, however rich, was the blazing Sacramento Valley, and very repulsive the city of Sacramento, which, at a distance of 125 miles from the Pacific, has an elevation of only thirty feet. The mercury stood at 103 degrees in the shade, and the fine white dust was stifling.

In the late afternoon we began the ascent of the Sierras*, whose sawlike points had been in sight for

30   many miles. The dusty fertility was all left behind, the country became rocky and gravelly, and deeply scored by streams bearing the muddy wash of the mountain gold mines down to the muddier Sacramento. There were long broken ridges and deep ravines, the ridges becoming longer, the ravines deeper, the pines thicker and larger, as

35   we ascended into a cool atmosphere of exquisite purity, and before 6 P.M. the last traces of cultivation* and the last hardwood trees were left behind.

Glossary:
Sandwich Islands — the name given to the Hawaiian Islands in 1778
cantaloupe — a type of melon
freightage — the transportation of goods in bulk
the Sierras — a mountain range in the Western United States
cultivation — growing and farming

Isabella Bird was an acclaimed explorer. She's renowned for the way she challenged Victorian society's expectations of women and how she even continued to travel despite her ill-health. She was also the first woman to become a fellow of the Royal Geographical Society — a professional centre for geographical learning in the UK.

Q1   Look again at lines 19-28.

a) Find an example of hyperbole used to describe the harvest in lines 19-25. What effect does this have on the reader?

....

....

....

....

b) What impression do you get of Sacramento and the Sacramento Valley in lines 25-28? How has Bird created this impression?

....

....

....

....

....

Q2   Look at the last paragraph. How does Bird create the sense that she's moving further and further away from society and civilisation on her journey up the Sierras?

....

....

....

....

....

....

....

....

Section Six — Getting Away From It All

Q3 A student reads the extract and says, "The overall tone of the extract is one of enthusiasm." Do you agree with this statement? Give examples to support your ideas.

....

....

....

....

....

....

....

Q4 You now need to refer only to lines 1-8.
How does the writer use language to describe the landscape?

PAPER 2 Q3

Make some notes in the box, then write your answer on a separate piece of paper.

Q5 You now need to refer only to lines 9-19.
How does the writer use language to describe San Francisco?

PAPER 2 Q3

Jot down some ideas in the box below, then write your answer on a separate piece of paper.

You don't have to agree with a statement...

If you're ever given a statement and asked whether you agree or disagree with it, feel free to give your honest response. These questions are all about your interpretation, so there are no right or wrong answers — just make sure that you have plenty of solid evidence from the extract to support your opinion.

© Not to be photocopied

Exercise B — The Exmoor Files

Extract B — From 'The Exmoor Files: How I Lost a Husband and Found Rural Bliss' by Liz Jones, 2009

Fashion journalist and newspaper columnist Liz Jones moved to Exmoor after her divorce in 2007. She wrote a book about the experience of beginning her new life in the countryside. This extract comes from the start of that book, where Jones is arriving at her new home for the first time.

After a fraught four-hour drive from London, with Snoopy in his basket on the front seat glaring at me accusingly, Sweetie, Susie and Squeaks on the back seat, all in a row, heads bobbing, like the Three Degrees*, I finally, after following the raging, bubbling River Exe and then the River Barle for about an hour, in a blizzard of falling red, gold and burnt umber* leaves, turn into a lane, my lane. The hedgerows

5 are full of bright green ferns, and brambles scratch at the side of my BMW convertible; I don't know whether to be cross or pleased. The middle of the lane is muddy and full of grass, which I take as a good sign. No one ever comes this way, I think. When I was deciding whether or not to buy the house, and wondering if it would be safe for my cats, the lane was, I thought, the next best thing to a moat. No one will ever find me. I can, at last, be completely and utterly on my own.

10 I bump across a cattle grid and am now, officially, in Exmoor National Park. I should, I suppose, shout 'Hurrah!' But instead I merely wind down my window and stick my head out in the cold, crisp air. I breathe in, slowly. I can taste a mixture of earth, moss, leaf mould and some sort of cow. It's now five in the evening and almost dark. I set off again and after a few miles I come to a fork in the road. I stick the car in neutral. I think, Jesus, it's foggy, I'm *doomed*, but then realise it's just my exhaust fumes. I am

15 literally (well, not literally, but almost) at a crossroads in my life. I take the left fork, with its rickety sign that points to not only my new farm but to my brand-new life, and crunch slowly, tentatively, beneath a disused railway bridge and start my climb up a steep, treacherous hill, excitement mounting in my chest like a burp. I turn left again and arrive at the five-bar gate. My gate. I stop the car, get out, carefully closing my car door in case my cats, Houdini*-fashion, escape from their cages and run for the hills. I open the

20 gate. I crunch along the drive, taking in the oak trees ('My oak trees!') and sycamores ('My sycamores!') and horse chestnuts and park in an old bit of barn that's leaning ominously. ('How nice not to drive round and round for hours looking for a place to park! This is so easy!') I decide to leave the cats safely locked in the car for now, and walk up to the house. Everything is pretty gloomy. I teeter on the cobbles and see a man with a clipboard hopping by the front porch.

25 'Welcome!' the man shouts with what turns out to be false cheer; he looks about 12. He's the estate agent. I notice there are sheep in my fields, which are so green they are fluorescent and hurt my eyes. 'Why are there sheep in my fields?' I ask him as he unlocks the door, which is huge, wooden and ancient. And scuffed. There are sheep skulls hung in the porch.

The house, which back in the August sunshine had
30 looked charming and olde worlde, covered in ivy, with stone mullion windows*, now looks as though it's about to fall down. Why hadn't I noticed this when I looked round?

> Glossary:
> the Three Degrees — an American female vocal group formed in the 1960s
> burnt umber — dark reddish-brown
> Houdini — a famous illusionist and escape artist
> mullion windows — windows that have vertical divides between the window panes

Q1 In line 8, Jones describes the lane leading to the house as "the next best thing to a moat." What does this tell you about the house?

....

....

....

Q2 How would you describe the style of this extract?
What techniques does Jones use to create this style?

....

....

....

....

....

....

....

Q3 You now need to refer only to lines 18-33.
How does the writer use language to describe the farm?

PAPER 2
Q3

Make some notes in the box, then write your answer on a separate piece of paper.

Style can have a big effect on how someone responds to a text...

The style of a text is made up of lots of different features, such as language, structure and tone. All of these have an effect on the reader, so think about an extract's overall style and how the writer wants you to feel.

Exercise C — Comparing Texts

Q1 Do you think the purpose of each text is similar or different? Explain your answer using examples from both texts.

Extract A was originally written by Bird as part of a personal letter to a family member.

....

....

....

....

....

....

....

....

Q2 Compare how the writers convey their different feelings and perspectives about being away from the city.

PAPER 2
Q4

Make a plan in the space below, then write your answer on a separate piece of paper.

In your answer, you could:

- compare their different feelings and perspectives
- compare the methods the writers use to convey their different feelings and perspectives
- support your response with references to both texts.

Extension Activity

WRITING TASK

Write a paragraph or two describing a city or town, then write some describing the countryside. Remember to use lots of language devices in each description. When you've written about both, compare the passages. You should think about the mood, images and adjectives you've used.

Exercise A — Partnership for a Healthier America

Extract A — Abridged from a speech given by Michelle Obama at The Partnership for a Healthier America Summit, 2015

During her time as the First Lady of the United States, Michelle Obama led a health campaign called Let's Move! Its objective was to reduce childhood obesity and promote healthier lifestyles. This extract is taken from a speech she made celebrating five years of the Let's Move! campaign.

I want to thank all of you. Many of you were out there fighting for our kids' health long before I came to this issue as First Lady. And I just want you to know how grateful I am to all of you and how inspired I am by you. And I am so proud to be with you today as we kick off the fifth anniversary — five years — of Let's Move! Five years! Feels like my child. How fast they grow.

5   Now, our theme for this anniversary is "Celebrate, Challenge, Champion." We are celebrating how far we've come. We're challenging ourselves to do even more. And we're committing to be true champions for this issue for the next five years and beyond. And I want to start off today by doing a little celebrating, because over the past five years, we have truly changed the culture around healthy eating and living in this country.

Just think about how much things have changed. Food companies are racing like never before to create
10   healthier versions of their products. Even convenience stores are selling fruits and vegetables. Head to the local drive-thru, and kids' meals might include apples and skim milk. Schools are growing gardens. They're moving beyond just pizza and tater tots to lunches filled with fresh produce and whole grains. Companies are actually rewarding employees for eating right and going to the gym. Five years ago, all this stuff would have been considered cutting-edge, but now, today, it's our new norm.

15   For years, doctors and nurses had been sounding the alarm as younger and younger kids were developing diabetes* and high blood pressure. Businesses were struggling with rising health care costs. Parents were anxious about their kids' health and self-esteem. Most of these folks didn't have big marketing budgets or special interests lobbying* for them in Washington*, so too often, their concerns simply weren't being heard. But together, we helped give them a voice. Together, we helped them take on this issue in their homes, in their
20   schools and in their communities. And the results have been beyond anything we could have ever imagined.

Childhood obesity rates have finally stopped rising, and obesity rates are actually falling among our youngest children. But let's be clear: While the progress we've made is impressive, it's also incredibly fragile. And despite this progress, you know the statistics are still daunting. About one in three kids in this country today is still overweight or obese. We still spend nearly $200 billion a year on obesity-related health care costs — and
25   that figure will jump to nearly $350 billion a year by 2018.

And this is really where the "Challenge" part of our anniversary theme comes in. Because if we start to lose focus, then we will go right back to where we started. Because plenty of folks out there are just waiting for us to get complacent or bored and move on to the next trendy issue. So we've got our work cut out for us. And I want to be very clear: I have no intention of slowing down on this issue. I do not have a one- or two-year
30   horizon for this work. I have a rest-of-my-life horizon, and I know that all of you do too. Because that's what it's going to take.

And that brings me to the "Champion" part of our fifth anniversary theme. Because that's what it means to truly be a champion for our kids. It means investing for the long term.

These kids are our future. They're our future workforce, our
35   future innovators and leaders and dreamers. And as parents, there is nothing we would not do for them — nothing. So as a country, we should meet that exact same standard. We should do everything we possibly can to give our kids every chance to fulfil their boundless potential — every chance.

Glossary:
diabetes — a medical condition that results in a person's blood sugar levels being too high
lobbying — attempting to influence those with the power to make decisions
Washington — referring to Washington D.C., the capital city of the USA and the centre of the country's political activity

Q1   In the first two paragraphs, Michelle Obama introduces healthy eating as the topic of the speech.

a) Give two examples from the first paragraph where Obama uses language
    to appeal to her audience. Explain why you think each one has this effect.

    1. ....

    ....

    ....

    2. ....

    ....

    ....

b) "Celebrate, Challenge, Champion" (line 5) is a list of three. Why does Obama use this device?

    ....

    ....

    ....

Q2   Briefly summarise Obama's argument in the third paragraph of the extract.

....

....

....

....

Q3   Look at the extract as a whole. How does Obama use structure to draw the audience in?

....

....

....

....

....

....

Section Seven — Food for Thought

First Lady is the title traditionally given to the wife of the US President. In recent history, the role of First Lady of the United States has changed to mean that they are now expected to have a greater involvement in the political scene and lead campaigns to improve American society.

Q4 A student reads this extract and says, "Michelle Obama was only involved in Let's Move! because it was her duty as First Lady." How far do you agree with this statement? Use evidence from the extract to support your view.

....

....

....

....

....

....

....

....

....

....

Q5 You now need to refer only to lines 15-25.
How does the writer use language to describe children's health?

PAPER 2
Q3

Jot down some ideas in the box below, then write your answer on a separate piece of paper.

Remember to think about the form of the text...

When you're reading an extract, always consider its form. For example, if you're analysing a speech, look out for any features or devices which you think would be particularly effective when the text is read aloud.

© Not to be photocopied

Exercise B — The Idle Thoughts of an Idle Fellow

Extract B — Adapted from 'The Idle Thoughts of an Idle Fellow' by Jerome K. Jerome, 1886

This extract is taken from a collection of humorous essays by the English writer Jerome K. Jerome. The essays were first published in a magazine, before they were compiled into a book. They record Jerome's comic observations on everything from pets and the weather, to eating and drinking.

I always was fond of eating and drinking, even as a child — especially eating, in those early days. I had an appetite then, also a digestion. I remember a dull-eyed, red-faced gentleman coming to dine at our house once. He watched me eating for about five minutes, quite fascinated seemingly, and then he turned to my father with — "Does your boy ever suffer from dyspepsia*?"

5 "I never heard him complain of anything of that kind," replied my father. "Do you ever suffer from dyspepsia, Colly wobbles*?" (They called me Colly wobbles, but it was not my real name.)

"No, pa," I answered. After which I added: "What is dyspepsia, pa?"

My red-faced friend regarded me with a look of mingled amazement and envy. Then in a tone of infinite pity he slowly said: "You will know — some day."

10 My poor, dear mother used to say she liked to see me eat, and it has always been a pleasant reflection to me since that I must have given her much gratification in that direction. A growing, healthy lad, taking plenty of exercise and careful to restrain himself from indulging in too much study, can generally satisfy the most exacting expectations as regards his feeding powers.

It is amusing to see boys eat when you have not got to pay for it. Their idea of a square meal is a pound
15 and a half of roast beef with five or six good-sized potatoes, plenty of greens, and four thick slices of Yorkshire pudding, followed by a couple of currant dumplings, a few green apples, a penny's worth of nuts, half a dozen jumbles*, and a bottle of ginger-beer. After that they play at horses.

How they must despise us men, who require to sit quiet for a couple of hours after dining off a spoonful of clear soup and the wing of a chicken!

20 A good dinner brings out all the softer side of a man. Under its genial influence the gloomy and morose become jovial and chatty. Sour, starchy individuals, who all the rest of the day go about looking as if they lived on vinegar and Epsom salt*, break out into smiles after dinner, and exhibit a tendency to pat small children on the head and to talk to them — vaguely — about sixpences. Serious men thaw and become mildly cheerful, and snobbish young men of the heavy-mustache type forget to make
25 themselves objectionable.

Hunger is a luxury to us, a piquant*, flavor-giving sauce. It is well worth while to get hungry and thirsty merely to discover how much gratification can be obtained from eating and drinking. If you wish to thoroughly enjoy your dinner, take a thirty-mile country walk after breakfast and don't touch anything till you get back. How your eyes will glisten at sight of the white table-cloth and steaming dishes then!
30 With what a sigh of content you will put down the empty beer tankard and take up your knife and fork! And how comfortable you feel afterward as you push back your chair and beam round upon everybody.

Ah! we may talk sentiment as much as we like, but the stomach is the real seat of happiness in this world. The kitchen is the chief temple wherein we worship, its roaring fire is our vestal flame*,
35 and the cook is our great high-priest. He is a mighty magician and a kindly one. He soothes away all sorrow and care. He drives forth all hatred, gladdens all love. Our God is great and the cook is his prophet. Let us eat, drink, and be merry.

Glossary:
dyspepsia — indigestion
collywobbles — stomach pain
jumbles — a type of biscuit
Epsom salt — a multi-purpose salt
piquant — pleasantly spicy
vestal flame — sacred fire

Most of Jerome K. Jerome's writing is humorous. He became very well-known for his satire (comic writing which normally criticises people or ideas) and was even appointed as editor of a satirical magazine, called *The Idler*.

Q1 Jerome uses humour in his writing. What effect does this have? Use an example from the extract to support your answer.

....

....

....

....

Q2 Jerome talks about the effect of food and hunger in the extract.

a) What does Jerome mean by "sour, starchy individuals" (line 21)? What is the effect of this phrase?

....

....

....

b) Why do you think Jerome uses exclamations in lines 29-30?

....

....

....

Q3 You now need to refer only to lines 32-38. How does the writer use language to describe cooking?

PAPER 2 Q3

Write down some thoughts in the box below, then write your answer on a separate piece of paper.

Always be on the lookout for subtle features in the text...

Subtle features like irony and sarcasm aren't always easy to spot, but they're useful to comment on, so keep an eye out for them. Often the tone of a text can help you decide if things are ironic or sarcastic.

Exercise C — Comparing Texts

Q1 Compare the style and tone of both extracts. Think about the effect they have on the reader.

....

....

....

....

....

....

....

....

Q2 Compare how the writers convey their different perspectives on eating.

PAPER 2 Q4

In your answer, you could:
- compare their different perspectives on eating
- compare the methods the writers use to convey their different perspectives
- support your response with references to both texts.

Plan your answer in the space below, then write it on a separate piece of paper.

Extension Activity

WRITING TASK

Food is an extremely popular topic — from cookery books and restaurant reviews to food travel writing. Write a description of your favourite meal or restaurant, or even a memory associated with food. Remember to include plenty of detail and vivid language to engage the reader.

Section Seven — Food for Thought

Exercise A — Advice to a Young Man

Extract A — Abridged from 'Advice to a Young Man Upon First Going to Oxford' by Reverend Edward Berens, 1832

This extract is taken from a collection of letters which Reverend Edward Berens wrote to offer advice to future students of the University of Oxford. Although he had several nephews who attended the university (the letters are addressed to them), they were also intended for others in their situation.

MY DEAR NEPHEW,

I do not know exactly what allowance your father has been able to give you, but whatever it may be, I trust that you are resolutely determined to keep within it. This will, of course, require a good deal of care and attention. Many young men, when, upon going to the University, they find in their pockets a much
5   larger sum than they ever possessed before, fancy themselves rich, and at liberty to allow themselves various unnecessary indulgences. The consequence is, that they become entangled in debts, from which they can never extricate* themselves during their continuance at Oxford. Be on your guard against getting thus hampered. Take it for granted, that the regular and necessary claims upon your finances will leave but little over for the indulgence of pleasure or fancy.

10   The expenses of an University education are often most unfairly exaggerated by writers and speakers, who are fond of running down all old institutions. They seem to forget that, wherever a young man may be, he must eat and drink, and must purchase clothes suitable to his station in society. I was myself, as you probably know, at Christ Church*, where I took my degree, and afterwards became a Fellow of Oriel*. At Oriel, (which may probably be taken as a fair average of the rest of the University,) the *necessary*
15   annual expenses of a commoner are from 70*l.** to 80*l.*, or thereabouts. This includes room-rent, batels, (that is, breakfast, dinner, etc. *exclusive* of tea and sugar), tuition, University and College dues, coals, letters, washing, servants. The University dues are less than 1*l.* per annum. There are, perhaps, few places in England, where a gentleman can be comfortably lodged and boarded at a much cheaper rate. Still there will always be many incidental expenses, and you must put in practice a pretty severe economy* in order
20   to meet them.

In the manner in which you spend your money, as in every thing else, accustom yourself to a certain degree of self-denial. Do not buy any thing merely because it hits your fancy, and you think you should *like to have it*, but consider whether you cannot easily *do without it*. Be as liberal as you can reasonably afford to be in assisting others, especially the poor, but spend as little as you can help upon yourself.
25   Above all, never buy, or order, any thing which you are unable to pay for.

The habit of running in debt is pregnant with evil and misery of every description. It often — perhaps generally — amounts to positive dishonesty. The money which you owe a tradesman is really his property. The articles, which you have received from him, are hardly your own, until you have paid for them. If you keep them, without paying for them when the seller
30   wishes and asks for payment, you deprive a man of that which belongs to him; and is not that something approaching to robbery? To a man possessed of proper feeling and a nice sense of honour, it must be very painful to suffer a tradesman to ask twice for
35   what is clearly his right.

> Glossary:
> extricate — to free from a situation
> Christ Church — a college at the University of Oxford
> Fellow of Oriel — a figure of authority at Oriel,
> which is a college at the University of Oxford
> l. — an old version of the pound sign (£)
> economy — in this context, an attempt to save money

Q1 Read again the first part of Extract A, from lines 1-9. Choose four statements below which are true.

PAPER 2 Q1

A Berens does not know how much money his nephew will have. ☐

E Students can easily pay off debts they incur at university. ☐

B Berens thinks students can easily manage their finances. ☐

F Berens thinks his nephew should take his allowance for granted. ☐

C Many new students are not used to having so much money. ☐

G Beren warns that students have to pay several regular bills. ☐

D Berens claims students spend money on things they don't need. ☐

H Berens's nephew will have lots of money left after buying essentials. ☐

Q2 Read lines 12-17. What is the effect of Berens writing about his own experiences?

....

....

....

....

Reverend Edward Berens was a Fellow of Oriel College. As a Fellow, he would have been part of the group that managed Oriel and would also have been entitled to certain privileges within the college.

Q3 Now consider the extract as a whole.

a) Briefly summarise Berens's viewpoint on the cost of going to university.

....

....

....

....

....

b) Do you think that Berens's viewpoint could be biased? Explain why or why not.

....

....

....

....

Section Eight — On the Money

Q4 Edward Berens writes with an authoritative tone in this extract.
Explain how Berens achieves this tone. Do you think it's effective?

....

....

....

....

....

....

....

....

....

....

....

....

Q5 You now need to refer only to lines 26-35.
How does the writer use language to describe debt?

PAPER 2
Q3

Make some notes in the box, then write your answer on a separate piece of paper.

Think carefully when you're summarising an argument...

Summarising a writer's viewpoint can be tricky. Don't try and tackle it from memory — re-read the extract as a whole and take some time to make sure that you understand everything the writer is saying.
Then, underline or jot down the points that you think are key to the writer's opinion. If there are points which lead on from (or contradict) one another, you can reflect this in how you structure your answer.

Exercise B — How to Keep a Budget While at Uni

Extract B — 'How to keep to a budget while at uni' from The Good Universities Guide, 2013
This article is from an Australian website which gives advice and information about universities.

If you think being a student means being poor, think again! With careful planning and a little self-restraint, you can learn to keep to a budget and not skimp on life's necessities.

Set a budget

5 If the thought of drawing up a spreadsheet or tracking your purchases makes you cringe, you may just need to grin and bear it. It can be helpful to map out your major weekly, monthly or yearly expenses in advance (car insurance, rent and petrol, for example) and see how these fit in with your savings — especially if they are clumped together in one month, or worse, in one week. Setting aside an amount for emergencies means that if you're suddenly hit with an unexpected expense, such as a large phone bill, you will be more prepared. As you plan your budget, this is a great time to think about any areas

10 where you can cut back to save money; while expenses such as rent are a necessity, weekly outings and designer clothes are not.

Prepare meals at home

This is a student budgeting staple. While takeaway meals are quick and delicious, the cost really does accumulate over time. Even the relatively small cost of a takeaway latté can add up — a coffee each

15 weekday over four weeks can cost more than $70!

Even if you only commit to taking your own lunch to uni (whether you make a sandwich or snap up dinner leftovers), you will find yourself saving upwards of $40–50 per week. You can even draw up a cooking roster* or pre-make and freeze meals to eat throughout the week, which will save you both time and money. When you do go out for lunch or dinner, look for cheaper options — splitting a pizza

20 or dumpling dish with a friend are both good examples. And remember, pubs and bars may also offer discounts when you show your student card.

Learn to 'shop smart'

Whether you're buying food, clothes or even heading out with friends, a little bit of smart shopping can pay off in the long run — and doesn't mean always saying 'no'. Instead, you might do some research to

25 see which stores offer student discounts or how prices compare between your local supermarket and the nearby fruit and veg market. You might also find that certain nights of the week (cheap Tuesday) are more 'budget friendly'.

Take advantage of second-hand options

This includes anything from clothing and furniture to electronics and textbooks. You'll be surprised at

30 how much you can save. A brand new textbook, for example, can cost around $100 (more if you are studying a theory-heavy degree). Purchasing a second-hand copy from a past student is guaranteed to save you money (especially if the book goes untouched until exam time). You can also scope out garage sales or local markets and snap up a few bargains — or better yet, contact the market

35 organiser and set up your own stall to earn some cash.

> Glossary:
> roster — a plan detailing when people should carry out a particular task

48

Q1 Look at the extract as a whole.

a) How would you describe the tone of this extract?

....

....

b) How does the writer use language to create this tone?

....

....

....

....

....

....

c) Do you think this tone would appeal to the writer's intended audience? Why?

....

....

....

....

....

Q2 You now need to refer only to lines 3-15.
How does the writer use language to describe budgeting?

(PAPER 2 Q3)

Jot down some ideas in the box below, then write your answer on a separate piece of paper.

Make sure you pay attention to the layout...

As well as analysing the language of an article, it's important to look at its layout. There could be lots to comment on — it might have a headline to grab the reader's attention, or subheadings to split up the text.

Exercise C — Comparing Texts

Q1 Tick the correct box to show which extract each fact relates to.

	Extract A	Extract B	Both
A Students should set aside money for unexpected costs.	☐	☐	☐
B Students should prioritise necessities.	☐	☐	☐
C Renting university accommodation is comparatively cheap.	☐	☐	☐
D Cooking at home is a good way of saving money.	☐	☐	☐
E Budgeting can involve making money as well as spending it.	☐	☐	☐
F The cost of being at university is sometimes exaggerated.	☐	☐	☐

Q2 Compare how the writers convey their different attitudes to spending money at university.

PAPER 2 Q4

In your answer, you could:
- compare their different attitudes
- compare the methods the writers use to convey their different attitudes
- support your response with references to both texts.

Use the box below to make a plan, then write your answer on a separate piece of paper.

Extension Activity

Both extracts advise, but they approach their audiences differently. Write a short article advising people on a topic that is important to you. When you're writing, remember to consider your target audience and the effect that the linguistic and structural devices you include will have.

Exercise A — London Characters

Extract A — Abridged from 'London Characters and the Humorous Side of London Life', 1871

London experienced great growth in the 19th century, both economically and in its population. This extract, written anonymously, describes life in London compared to village life at the time.

A man's first residence in London is a revolution in his life and feelings. He loses at once no small part of his individuality. He was a man before, now he is a "party". No longer known as Mr. Brown, but as (say) No. XXI., he feels as one of many cogs in one of the many wheels of an incessantly wearing, tearing, grinding, system of machinery. His country notions must be modified, and all his life-long ways

5   and takings-for-granted prove crude and questionable. He is hourly reminded "This is not the way in London; that this won't work here". Custom rules everything, and custom never before seemed to him half as strange, strong, or inexorable*. The butcher always cuts one way and the greengrocer serves him with equal rigour. His orders never before seemed of so little importance. The independence and the take-it-or-leave-it indifference of the tradesmen contrast strongly with the obsequiousness* of the

10   country shop. However great a customer before he feels a small customer now. The tradesman is shorter and more saving of his words. He serves, takes your money, and turns away to some one else, whereas in the country they indulge you with a little talk into the bargain.

Many other things contribute to make our new Londoner feel smaller in his own eyes. The living stream flows by him in the streets; he never saw so many utter strangers to him and to each other before; their

15   very pace and destination are different; there is a walk and business determination distinctly London. In other towns men saunter they know not whither, but nearly every passer-by in London has his point, and is making so resolutely towards it that it seems not more his way than his destination as he is carried on with the current; and of street currents there are two, to the City and from the City, so distinct and persistent, that our friend can't get out of one without being jostled by the other. In the country

20   Dr. Jones drives in one day, Mr. and Mrs. Robinson and family walk in the next. Sometimes fifty people may be counted, sometimes ten, but in London there is an ebb and flow in the Strand* as regular and uniform as in the Thames. The City noise begins gradually about six with the sweeps and the milk-pails amongst the earliest calls, though ponderous* market-carts and night cabs are late and early both. This fitful rumble deepens to a steady roar about nine, and there is no approach to silence till night, and after

25   a very short night of repose the same roar awakens again; so City people live as in a mill, till constant wearing sound becomes to them the normal state of nature.

There is a good deal of education in all this. The mind is ever on the stretch with rapid succession of new images, new people, and new sensations. All business is done with an increased pace. The buying and the selling, the counting and the weighing, and even

30   the talk over the counter, is all done with a degree of rapidity and sharp practice which brightens up the wits of this country cousin more than any books or schooling he ever enjoyed.

Glossary:
inexorable — unstoppable, relentless
obsequiousness — eager to help someone
the Strand — a major street in Central London
ponderous — slow-moving and heavy

Q1　In the first paragraph, the writer begins to describe what living in London feels like.

a) Find a simile from this part of the extract and explain the impression it gives you of life in London.

....

....

....

....

....

....

....

b) How does the writer use language elsewhere in this paragraph to create
this impression of London? Give examples from the text.

....

....

....

....

....

....

Q2　How does the tone of the extract change in the third paragraph?
Explain how the writer creates this tonal shift.

....

....

....

....

....

....

....

　　　　　　　　　　　　　　　　Section Nine — Heading to the Capital

There was a big difference between the population of cities and villages in nineteenth-century Britain as many people started moving to large cities to find jobs. This left village populations low, while in London the population increased to nearly 7 million by the end of the century.

Q3   The writer describes city life and country life throughout the extract.

a) Summarise two differences the writer gives between city life and country life.

1. ....

....

2. ....

....

b) Do you think the writer prefers city life or country life? Explain why you think this.

....

....

....

....

....

....

Q4   You now need to refer only to lines 13-26. How does the writer use language to describe the people of London?

(PAPER 2 Q3)

Write down some thoughts in the box below, then write your answer on a separate piece of paper.

Knowing what the 19th century was like may help you out...

You don't need to know specific facts about the 19th century, but if you have some knowledge of what life was like then, it will help you understand the context of texts like this and make them easier to analyse.

Exercise B — Londoners

Extract B — Abridged from 'Londoners' by Craig Taylor, 2011

This extract comes from the introduction of a book about people's experiences of living in London. It recalls Taylor's personal experience of living in London a few months after moving from Canada.

Again I was living with someone else's furniture, carpets and net curtains. The Portuguese shop beneath the flat sold custard tarts and dusty salt fish. Portuguese men congregated in the room at the back and occasionally the owner left the door open an inch, so I would see them sitting, hands clasped, speaking quietly, on mornings when I came downstairs for a puffed, doughy croissant. There are half-opened doors
5 everywhere in London, and some days I glimpsed inside the clubs of St James's Square; I saw the paintings on the wall of the Garrick; the smoke hanging above the pool tables in Dalston's old Fenerbahce Social Club. There were only so many doors I could pass through in London, even if I knocked on them all.

My visa expired. The day slipped past silently. I checked with a lawyer, and she advised me to fly out of the country immediately so that I would not be an overstayer, a weighty term in the world of immigration
10 law. I left immediately and slept on a friend's couch in Toronto. She asked me if I was going back, and how I felt about London. I contorted with each answer. I felt a mixture of love, ambivalence and loathing. Back in Canada, I remembered what it was like to live in a village, to walk under dark skies, to hear the rustle of trees and experience the consistent tempo, the pace, of life. It made sense when days had mornings and afternoons, and weeks had Sunday rituals. I understood that this is how life plays out. Growth, family,
15 death. Yet all this can be dispensed with in London. It encourages defiance. I missed what it gave me, who it allowed me to be. In London, on the rare nights I could afford a minicab home, I rolled down the window and watched the lights on the Thames. Most late-night minicabbers reaffirmed their love of the city with the same view. I loved its messiness, its attempts at order. I loved the anonymity it afforded.

Most of all I missed its energy. London is propulsion, it rewards those people who push forward. I
20 remembered my disappointment at walking in New York and reaching the water, the point of turning around. In London, even on the days when my knees hurt, my hip hurt and my Achilles tendon hurt, I could keep going. I could push on.

I wasn't an Anglophile*. My accent wasn't giving way to transatlanticism. I didn't want London as accoutrement*, to be the guy who used to live there, advising my parents' retired friends on tourist
25 itineraries. I just wanted to be back.

It isn't a two-way relationship. It's no use thinking this place loses any sleep over me. It disgorges* people every day, sneezing black grime, heading back to other corners of the country or far corners of the world. In the last ten years, the foreign-born population of London was busy doubling in size, reaching almost 2.2 million people, almost a third of the city. In addition to the long-standing Irish, Indian, Jamaican and
30 Bangladeshi communities, there were suddenly many new immigrants from Nigeria, Slovenia, Ghana, Vietnam, Somalia. London is an accordion breathing in and out.

Somehow I was given permission to return. Armed with a single piece of paper from the Home Office, I remember bending my passport open to show the Heathrow immigration officer this incontrovertible* evidence that I belonged. It was masochism*; it was happiness, purpose, a decision, a path. There's
35 nothing like wandering around a city you've already left to define an internal change. I felt different: defiant, bold, victorious.

I didn't dare call myself a Londoner. But around that point I began to ask, who is? Who gets to choose? I began to feel as if I belonged. I guess secretly I was attaching another very
40 inclusive definition to the word 'Londoners': if a person could get there, could stay there by whatever means possible, they could be a Londoner.

Glossary:
Anglophile — someone who really likes England
accoutrement — an accessory
disgorges — throws out or ejects
incontrovertible — unquestionable
masochism — enjoying something that is painful

Q1   What impression do the "half-opened doors" (line 4) give you of London? Why?

....

....

....

....

Q2   How has the text been structured to interest you as a reader?

....

....

....

....

....

....

....

....

Q3   You now need to refer only to lines 10-15.
How does the writer use language to describe life in a village?

PAPER 2
Q3

Jot down some ideas in the box below, then write your answer on a separate piece of paper.

A writer may focus on things beyond the main topic of the text...

Sometimes a writer may mention or describe something that isn't to do with the main focus of the text.
This is normally done for a reason. For example, a writer may have a paragraph about a hot summer's day
in a text about a white Christmas to create a contrast and emphasise the cold and snowy conditions.

Exercise C — Comparing Texts

Q1   Tick the correct box to show which extract each fact relates to.

	Extract A	Extract B	Both
A Newcomers must adapt when they arrive in London.	☐	☐	☐
B London is a multicultural city.	☐	☐	☐
C London has the power to make people who move there feel bold.	☐	☐	☐
D Customers don't receive friendly service in London.	☐	☐	☐
E The pace of life in London is faster than elsewhere.	☐	☐	☐

Q2   Compare how the writers convey their similar feelings and perspectives about London.   **PAPER 2 Q4**

In your answer, you could:
- compare their similar feelings and perspectives
- compare the methods the writers use to convey their similar feelings and perspectives
- support your response with references to both texts.

Use the box below to make a plan, then write your answer on a separate piece of paper.

WRITING TASK

Extension Activity

Many tourists visit new or exciting places, like big cities, to see the attractions. Imagine you work for a tourism company in a place you have visited or know well. Write a blog post encouraging people to visit. Think about the persuasive language you can use to entice people.

Section Nine — Heading to the Capital

Exercise A — Environmental Costs of Fast Fashion

Extract A — Abridged from 'The Environmental Costs of Fast Fashion' by Patsy Perry, from The Conversation, 2017

Dr Patsy Perry is a senior lecturer in Fashion Marketing at the University of Manchester. She has researched the impact fashion can have on the environment and ways of making it more sustainable.

It's tough to love our clothes and keep wearing them for longer when we are faced with a tempting array of newness on offer in the shops. But before you head out into the January sales for those irresistible deals, spare a thought for the impact of fast fashion on the environment.

5   Fast fashion focuses on speed and low costs in order to deliver frequent new collections inspired by catwalk looks or celebrity styles. But it is particularly bad for the environment as pressure to reduce cost and the time it takes to get a product from design to shop floor means that environmental corners are more likely to be cut. Criticisms of fast fashion include its negative environmental impact, water pollution, the use of toxic chemicals and increasing levels of textile waste.

Vibrant colours, prints and fabric finishes are appealing features of fashion garments, but many of these are

10   achieved with toxic chemicals. Textile dyeing is the second largest polluter of clean water globally, after agriculture. Greenpeace's* recent Detox campaign has been instrumental in pressuring fashion brands to take action to remove toxic chemicals from their supply chains, after it tested a number of brands' products and confirmed the presence of hazardous chemicals.

Hunger for newness

15   Textile waste is an unintended consequence of fast fashion, as more people buy more clothes and don't keep them as long as they used to. The international expansion of fast fashion retailers exacerbates* the problem on a global scale. Wardrobes in developed nations are saturated*, so in order to sell more products, retailers must tempt shoppers with constant newness and convince them the items they already have are no longer fashionable.

Increasing disposable income levels over recent generations means there is less need to "make do and mend", as

20   it's often cheaper and more convenient to buy new than have an item repaired. Busy lifestyles make many people more time-poor than previous generations, and with the loss of sewing and mending skills over time, there is less impetus* to repair our garments. The rise of supermarket fashion that can be purchased alongside the weekly shop and the regular occurrence of seasonal sales make clothing seem "disposable" in a way it didn't used to be.

There is interest in moving towards a more circular model of textile production which reuses materials wherever

25   possible, yet current recycling rates for textiles are very low. Despite a long-established national network of charity shops and increasing numbers of in-store recycling points in UK high-street stores, three-quarters of Britons throw away unwanted clothing, rather than donating or recycling it.

What shoppers can do

So, can consumers reduce the environmental cost of fast fashion when out shopping? Choosing an eco-friendly

30   fabric is complex as there are pros and cons to all fibre types. Garments which are labelled as being made from natural fibres are not necessarily better than synthetic, as fibre choice is only one part of a complex picture. Fibres still have to be spun, knitted or woven, dyed, finished, sewn and transported – all of which have different environmental impacts.

For example, choosing organic fabrics is better than choosing non-organic fabrics in terms of the chemicals used

35   to grow the fibres, but organic cotton still requires high amounts of water and the impact of dyeing it is higher than the impact of dyeing polyester.

Recycled content is often best of all, as it reduces the pressure on virgin resources and tackles the growing problem of waste management.

The Love Your Clothes initiative from the charity WRAP gives information

40   for consumers on each stage of the purchase process, from buying smarter, to caring for and repairing items, to upcycling or customisation, and finally responsible disposal. Ultimately, the best thing we can do is to keep our clothing in use for longer – and buy less new stuff.

> Glossary:
> Greenpeace — an organisation that promotes environmental awareness
> exacerbates — makes something worse
> saturated — full
> impetus — encouragement to act

Q1   Read again the first part of Extract A, from lines 1-13.
Choose four statements below which are true.

PAPER 2
Q1

A   Patsy Perry thinks it is easy to keep
wearing clothes you already own.   ☐

E   Critics say fast fashion causes
environmental damage.   ☐

B   Fast fashion relies on
speed and high costs.   ☐

F   Agriculture is the biggest global
polluter of clean water.   ☐

C   Fast fashion involves
producing new collections.   ☐

G   Activists have encouraged fashion
brands to change their practices.   ☐

D   Fashion shows and celebrity culture
have no impact on fast fashion.   ☐

H   Campaigners have found hazardous
chemicals in fast fashion products.   ☐

Q2   Why is it likely that clothing manufacturers do not prioritise methods that are
good for the environment? Use evidence from the text to support your argument.

....

....

....

....

....

....

Q3   "Patsy Perry doesn't sympathise with people who buy fast fashion." To what extent
do you agree with this statement? Explain why, using examples to support your view.

....

....

....

....

....

....

....

....

....

....

Section Ten — Fashionable Thoughts

Q4 Patsy Perry wrote this article for *The Conversation*, a website that publishes material written by academics and researchers. Its purpose is to inform its readers.

a) How does the writer use language to achieve this purpose? Give examples from the text.

....

....

....

....

....

....

b) How does the structure of the text help to achieve this purpose? Explain your answer.

....

....

....

....

....

....

....

....

Q5 You now need to refer only to lines 9-18.
How does the writer use language to describe the fashion industry?

PAPER 2
Q3

Make some notes in the box, then write your answer on a separate piece of paper.

Individual words and phrases can be analysed in great detail...

Writers take great care in selecting specific words and phrases. It's often worthwhile analysing their word choices in detail as they can give you a lot of information. For example, they may help you work out the writer's opinions or tell you something about the impression the writer wants to create for the reader.

Exercise B — Caper-Sauce

Extract B — Adapted from 'Caper-Sauce: A Volume of Chit-Chat About Men, Women, and Things' by Fanny Fern, 1872

Fanny Fern was an American novelist and the highest paid newspaper columnist in America in 1855. The book this extract is from is the sixth and last collection of columns she released.

It is curious with what different eyes human beings look upon new clothes, at different stages of existence. Youth, which least needs these auxiliaries*, is generally the most clamorous* for incessant change. Young men are as likely to be caught acting in this regard as their female counterpart. The new coat may squeeze; the new collar may strangle; the new boots may pinch; the new hat may leave its red

5 mark on the throbbing forehead, but perish the thought of not wearing either! From the days when our foremothers had their heads built up in turrets by the hurried hair-dresser, the night previous to some great festive occasion, and sat bolstered upright in bed all night, for fear of tumbling them — down to the present day of ladies' "hair-crimpers," human nature has held its own in this respect.

Middle age, with few exceptions, looks upon new clothes with abated* interest. Old clothes, like old

10 customs, fit easy. *Comfort*, anyhow, says middle age — appearances as the gods please; so new shoes lie on the shelf unworn for weeks, for fear of stiff heels or squeaky soles; and new clothes look and feel so spick-and-span and glossy, that middle age can not do a natural thing in them — middle age resents this petty, fretting intrusion on its much-loved quiet. It is irritable, till new clothes begin to *feel* easy, which is not generally the case till some seam grows threadbare, or some treacherous gap horrifies the

15 easy wearer with renewed visions of innovating fashions and fabrics.

Now this is very natural to a certain extent; but middle age sometimes forgets that something is due to affectionate young eyes, which take a proper pride in seeing "father" or "mother" neatly and becomingly dressed, according to their age and station in life.

It is a harrowing reflection how much money is "sunk" every day in new clothes, in which the blissfully

20 unconscious wearers look none the better, but rather the worse. Still, if everybody had good taste in this matter, there would be no foil* to the well-dressed; and I am afraid the heartless dry-goods* merchants care little whether blondes dress in orange color, or brunettes in sky-blue, so that their bills are paid.

But new clothes for the "baby." Ah! that is something worth while. I ask you, did love ever find fabric soft enough, or nice enough, or pretty enough, for "*the baby*"? Fathers and mothers may wish to make

25 as many economical decisions as they please; but why, if they mean to carry them out, do they linger at the shop-window where that dainty little satin bonnet stares them innocently in the face, with that pert little rosette, cocked upon one side, that "would look so cunning* on baby." Why do they contemplate the rows of bright little red boots, or the embroidered little sacques* and frocks? Why don't they cross right over and travel home out of the way of temptation?

30 Surely, no pink could rival the rose of baby's cheek; no crimson the coral of its lips; no blue the sapphire of its eyes. For all that, out comes the purse and home goes the bonnet, or cloak, or frock. Just as if shopkeepers didn't know that babies will keep on being born, and born pretty; and that

35 fathers and mothers are, and will be, their happy slaves all the world over to the end of time!

Glossary:
auxiliaries — helpers
clamorous — loud or demanding
abated — lessened
foil — someone who contrasts a person to highlight particular qualities in the other person
dry-goods — US term for clothing and textiles
cunning — cute or appealing
sacques — US term for a baby's jacket

Q1 How is the language used to describe the opinions of the young and middle-aged people different? Explain the effect this has.

....
....
....
....
....
....
....

Q2 How does Fern present merchants and parents? Use evidence from the extract in your answer.

....
....
....
....
....
....
....

Q3 You now need to refer only to lines 1-15.
How does the writer use language to describe new and old clothes?

PAPER 2
Q3

Jot down some ideas in the box below, then write your answer on a separate piece of paper.

You won't always know the topic of the extract inside and out...

It's possible that you'll come across extracts that talk about unfamiliar subjects. It's important not to panic, and to approach the extract as you normally would — read through the extract a couple of times and mark important words, phrases and other language devices. This should help to give you enough to analyse.

Exercise C — Comparing Texts

Q1 Compare how consumers are presented in each extract.

A consumer is someone who buys or uses something.

....

....

....

....

....

....

....

....

Q2 Compare how the writers convey their different attitudes to fashion.

PAPER 2 Q4

In your answer, you could:

- compare their different attitudes to fashion
- compare the methods the writers use to convey their different attitudes
- support your response with references to both texts.

Make a plan in the space below, then write your answer on a separate piece of paper.

Extension Activity

RESEARCH TASK

People tend to have different opinions about whether they enjoy shopping and fashion. Interview one person who likes shopping for clothes and another who dislikes it. Note the reasons they give, then consider the reasons for any similarities and differences in the language they use.

Exercise A — Travels in West Africa

Extract A — Abridged from 'Travels in West Africa' by Mary Kingsley, 1897

Mary Kingsley was an English explorer and travel writer. She visited remote African cultures alone, which was unusual for a Victorian woman, and lived with local people to learn about their lifestyles.

At high-water you do not see the mangroves* displaying their ankles in the way that shocked Captain Lugard. They look most respectable, their foliage rising densely in a wall irregularly striped here and there by the white line of an aërial root*, coming straight down into the water from some upper branch as straight as a plummet*, in the strange, knowing way an aërial root of a mangrove does, keeping the hard straight line until

5   it gets some two feet above water-level, and then spreading out into blunt fingers with which to dip into the water and grasp the mud. Banks indeed at high water can hardly be said to exist, the water stretching away into the mangrove swamps for miles and miles, and you can then go, in a suitable small canoe, away among these swamps as far as you please.

This is a fascinating pursuit. But it is a pleasure to be indulged in with caution; for one thing, you are certain

10   to come across crocodiles. Now a crocodile drifting down in deep water, or lying asleep with its jaws open on a sand-bank in the sun, is a picturesque adornment to the landscape when you are on the deck of a steamer, and you can write home about it and frighten your relations on your behalf; but when you are away among the swamps in a small dug-out canoe, and that crocodile and his relations are awake — a thing he makes a point of being at flood tide because of fish coming along — and when he has got his foot upon his

15   native heath — that is to say, his tail within holding reach of his native mud — he is highly interesting, and you may not be able to write home about him — and you get frightened on your own behalf; for crocodiles can, and often do, in such places, grab at people in small canoes. I have known of several natives losing their lives in this way; some native villages are approachable from the main river by a short cut, as it were, through the mangrove swamps, and the inhabitants of such villages will now and then go across this way with small

20   canoes instead of by the constant channel to the village, which is almost always winding. You are also liable to get tide-trapped in the swamps, the water falling round you when you are away in some lagoon, and you find you cannot get back to the main river. If you are a mere ordinary person of a retiring nature, like me, you stop in your lagoon until the tide rises again; most of your attention is directed to dealing with an "at home"* to crocodiles and mangrove flies, and with the fearful stench of the slime round you.

25   At corners here and there from the river face you can see the land being made from the waters. A mud-bank forms off it, a mangrove seed lights on it, and the thing's done. Well! not done, perhaps, but begun; for if the bank is high enough to get exposed at low water, this pioneer mangrove grows. He has a wretched existence though. You have only got to look at his dwarfed attenuated* form to see this. He gets joined by a few more bold spirits and they struggle on together, their network of roots stopping abundance of mud, and by good

30   chance now and then a consignment* of miscellaneous *débris* of palm leaves, or a floating tree-trunk, but they always die before they attain any considerable height. Still even in death they collect. Their bare white stems remaining like a net gripped in the mud, so that these pioneer mangrove heroes may be said to have laid down their lives to make that

35   mud-bank fit for colonisation, for the time gradually comes when other mangroves can and do colonise on it, and flourish, extending their territory steadily; and the mud-bank joins up with, and becomes a part of, Africa.

Glossary:
mangroves — trees that grow in swamps and shallow salt water
aërial root — a root that is above ground / water level
plummet — a line with a weight on it used to measure water depth
at home — a Victorian custom where women would only visit their friends at home at a set time and date
attenuated — incredibly thin
consignment — delivery

Q1   What do you think the purpose of this extract is? Why?

....
....
....
....
....

Q2   Summarise Kingsley's thoughts about canoeing through the mangrove swamps of West Africa.

....
....
....
....
....
....
....
....

Q3   How has the text been structured to interest you as a reader?

....
....
....
....
....
....
....
....

Q4 On line 22, Kingsley describes herself as "a mere ordinary person of a retiring nature".

a) What impression does this give the reader of Kingsley?

....

....

....

....

b) Do you think that Kingsley gives the reader an authentic account of her time in West Africa? Explain your answer.

....

....

....

....

....

....

....

....

....

Q5 You now need to refer only to lines 25-39.
How does the writer use language to describe the mangroves?

PAPER 2 Q3

Jot down some ideas in the box below, then write your answer on a separate piece of paper.

You can analyse sentences individually, as well as within paragraphs...

You can talk about individual sentences and the effect they have, as well as how writers use different sentences to make up paragraphs. For example, lots of simple sentences can be used to build tension. Keep an eye out for how writers use simple, compound and complex sentences in different ways.

Exercise B — Wildest Dreams

Extract B — Abridged from 'Wildest dreams: a family camping trip in Oman' by Fiona McAuslan, from The Guardian, 2017

Oman is a country in the Middle East that has a rapidly growing tourist industry. This extract describes the first leg of the writer and her family's week-long trip to the northeast of the country.

Camped out in the wilds of Oman's Al Jabal Al Akhdar mountain range, we were full of self-congratulation on finding the perfect spot. Yet while we were marvelling at the sunrise from atop a nearby peak, our campsite was being raided. Once we got back down we caught the culprits, a herd of mountain goats, red-handed: replete* with the honey, halwa* and fruit we had been saving for breakfast, they were reluctant to budge – even to the
5 tune of us banging picnic plates.

However, as perils of camping off the beaten track go, a hircine* invasion is fairly benign. Wild camping is legal in Oman: you can pitch your tent on any public land. From dramatic mountains to shimmering beaches, and miles and miles of golden dunes, Oman's natural beauty is a force to be reckoned with. Getting the tent pegs stuck in is the most rewarding way to see this Middle Eastern country.

10 Camping also offers a completely different view of the country from the one peddled by the tourist board and most tour operators. Tourism is on the rise in Oman, with the government pumping billions into luxury developments including a superyacht marina, five-star hotels and a replica of London's Westfield shopping mall, complete with English-style landscaping. The country hopes to attract 11.7 million visitors a year by 2040.

Desert camping could hardly be further from this opulence*. With little crime, and no natural predators, it is
15 also a safe option, so my partner and I had no qualms about taking our seven-year-old son. Inexhaustible energy levels in an only child means catching up on adult poolside reading is out. Our best family holidays are spent filling every moment with activity, so the busyness of camping is ideal. It's also the most affordable way to see this country, where holiday accommodation is often exorbitant*.

With a good selection of local companies hiring out camping equipment very cheaply, there was no need to bring
20 our own. I'd done a search and plumped for Nomad Travel, drawn by the naive simplicity of its website. Nomad Travel is run by Chris, an ex-pat* oilman who has been in Oman for decades, his wife Lorna and their son Josh.

Our plan was to take in three locations over a week. I wanted to experience the breathtaking solitude of the desert, my partner wanted mountain trekking, and our son yearned to play on a beach. Chris was going to lead the first part of the expedition. Usually he left the tours to one of the expert Omani guides he works with, but the
25 beach location was a favourite, discovered by him in his early days in Oman, and the nostalgia trip was too much for him to pass up.

First stop was the Wahiba Sands, about two hours south of capital city Muscat. Desert covers much of Oman (about 82% including the gravelly wadi valleys) and ranges from treacherous salt flats to stony planes, as well as the sweeping Arabian sands of cinematic legend. The heat and scale can be brutal and disorientating and the
30 tourist board advice is don't go it alone, but travel in a convoy of at least two 4WD cars – we were glad to have Chris with us.

There's an eerie beauty to the dunes. It's impossible to gaze across the knife-sharp edges of the empty peaks, sculpted by the collision of winds from the east and southern coast, and not have a sense of your own mortality. Some dunes tower nearly 100 metres high. In the heat, you could perish within hours without resources. Luckily,
35 we'd made a comfortable camp in the lee* of the dune on which I stood musing and, as the sun sunk low, we ate barbecued lamb kebabs prepared in advance for us by Lorna. Our son found a bleached goat skull when he was off gathering firewood, and we took turns setting up apocalyptic Instagram shots.

40 In my mind's eye, the desert sky jewelled with stars was going to be the trip's highlight but a glorious full moon put paid to that. It did bathe the dunes in a ghostly splendour, though, and we spotted a scarab beetle rolling its dung ball past the edge of the camp.

Glossary:
replete — well-fed, satisfied
halwa — a type of sweet foodstuff
hircine — relating to goats
opulence — luxury
exorbitant — extremely expensive
ex-pat — short for expatriate, someone who lives outside of their native country
lee — the side sheltered from the wind

Q1   How does the tone change throughout the first paragraph of the extract?

....

....

....

....

Q2   Look at lines 10-21. How do you think the writer feels about
the tourist industry? What is it that gives you this impression?

....

....

....

....

....

....

....

Q3   You now need to refer only to lines 27-43.
How does the writer use language to describe the desert?

PAPER 2
Q3

Write down some thoughts in the
box below, then write your answer
on a separate piece of paper.

Keep an eye out for implicit information...

Not every piece of information in a text will be stated explicitly — you may need to infer some things.
Use evidence from the extract and your own knowledge to work out any hidden meanings in the text.

Exercise C — Comparing Texts

Q1 Compare the overall style and tone of both extracts.
Write about the effect they have on the reader.

....

....

....

....

....

....

....

Q2 Compare how the writers convey their similar perspectives and feelings about travel.

PAPER 2
Q4

In your answer, you could:

- compare their similar perspectives and feelings
- compare the methods the writers use to convey their similar perspectives and feelings
- support your response with references to both texts.

Plan your answer in the space below, then
write it on a separate piece of paper.

Extension Activity

Ask friends and family members who have travelled to or explored somewhere to briefly describe their experiences. Compare their descriptions with those in the extracts. Do they differ in any way? Why do you think this is? Why do you think people used the language that they did?

Section Eleven — Intrepid Explorers

Exercise A — The Mastery of Languages

Extract A — Adapted from 'The Mastery of Languages' by Thomas Prendergast, 1864

Thomas Prendergast was a specialist in learning languages and wrote a number of books on the subject. In this extract, he explains how children learn language simply through hearing sentences spoken by others. He used this idea to create a method for learning several foreign languages.

A child, living in daily association with foreigners, acquires two or three languages at once, and speaks them all fluently and without intermixture. He learns them, not unconsciously nor without effort, but without tuition and without one idea of the nature of grammar. This is a feat which baffles the efforts of men of the best education.

5   Many conflicting and unsatisfactory reasons are proposed for the wonderful success of children. They include their greater power of concentration; their freedom from care, prejudice and distraction; their elasticity of mind; the flexibility of their vocal organs; their greater quickness and retentiveness of memory; their constantly hearing a language spoken, so learning by the aid of an ear uncorrupted; their greater delicacy of ear; and, finally, their having a brain unoccupied, and thus better adapted for the reception of
10   new words and ideas, like a sheet of paper, where what is first written, although covered by innumerable* new scribblings from day to day, is boldly asserted to be indestructible.

As children talk long before they are able to reason about words, some believe that the gift of speech is altogether independent of intellectual capabilities, and that it is merely the result of a physiological* function. Many contend that there can be no method in the process, because none is discernible*.

15   When children begin to compose a sentence which they have never heard uttered by others (or at least not often enough to enable them to retain it thoroughly), they speak with indecision and inaccuracy. But they occasionally utter complete sentences with fluency and accurate pronunciation when they are still incapable of understanding the principles of grammar. It is obvious, therefore, that they must have learned, retained, and reproduced these sentences by dint of imitation and reiteration.

20   These sentences are the rails on which the trains of thought travel swiftly, smoothly, and without the slightest deviation from their proper course; and each language seems to constitute a separate line of rails, because they do not clash with each other when the little linguists converse with two or more foreigners of different nations. This appears to be because the words are permanently bound together in those sentences which the child learns by imitation and repetition of the sounds.

25   Each new sentence which a child acquires is interchangeable, more or less usefully, with those previously learned; and as it will generally contain one or two already familiar words, an easy and natural connection springs up among them; they daily become more closely amalgamated* with each other in the memory, and at the same time more clearly and thoroughly understood.

Hence it appears that repetition is not only the process by which children originally acquire the power of
30   using sentences, but also the preserving principle by which children retain that power. By interchanging the words and the clauses, they utilize them all, and thus gradually, but unconsciously, expand their power of speech. They pronounce words to perfection by closely observing and mimicking the pitch of the voice, the tones, the gestures, the movements of the head, and the contortions of the face of those around them.

The success of children is due to their following the light of nature.
35   We have ignored that beacon, and have deviated from the right course; but when we obtain the true bearings, there is nothing to prevent us from resuming it, with every confidence of success.

> Glossary:
> innumerable — too many to be counted
> physiological — bodily
> discernible — noticeable
> amalgamated — combined

Q1 What is the effect of Prendergast's use of listing in the second paragraph?

....

....

....

....

....

....

Q2 What language device does Prendergast use across lines 10-11?
Explain what this part of the extract means and the effect it has on the reader.

....

....

....

....

....

....

....

....

Q3 Briefly summarise Prendergast's argument in the seventh paragraph.

....

....

....

....

....

....

Q4 The writer says "The success of children is due to their following the light of nature. We have ignored that beacon" (lines 34-35). What do you think this means? Explain why.

....

....

....

....

....

....

Q5 Look at the extract as a whole. How has the writer adapted their language to engage their audience?

....

....

....

....

....

....

....

Q6 You now need to refer only to lines 20-28.
How does the writer use language to describe sentences?

(PAPER 2 Q3)

Make some notes in the box, then write your answer on a separate piece of paper.

Make sure that you identify the intended audience...

If you're asked who you think the intended audience of an extract is, always try to make your answer as specific as possible. Think carefully about the topic of the extract, as well as the type of language and structure that the writer has used — use these to help you work out who they might be writing for.

Exercise B — Acting French

Extract B — Abridged from 'Acting French' by Ta-Nehisi Coates, from The Atlantic, 2014

Ta-Nehisi Coates is an American writer and journalist. In 2014, he attended a seven-week French language course at Middlebury College, an arts university in Vermont, USA. L'École Française, which translates as 'The French School', is an intensive summer school programme. The tutors there use teaching methods that help students become fluent in the French language quickly.

I spent the majority of this summer at Middlebury College, studying at l'École Française. I had never been to Vermont. I have not been many places at all. I did not have an adult passport until I was 37 years old. Sometimes I regret this. And then sometimes not. Learning to travel when you're older allows you to be young again, to touch the childlike amazement that is so often dulled away by adult

5 things. In the past year, I have seen more of the world than at any point before, and thus, I have been filled with that juvenile feeling more times then I can count — at a train station in Strasbourg, in an old Parisian bookstore, on a wide avenue in Lawndale. It was no different in Vermont where the green mountains loomed like giants. I would stare at these mountains out of the back window of the Davis Family Library. I would watch the clouds, which, before the rain, drooped over the mountains like

10 lampshades, and I would wonder what, precisely, I had been doing with my life.

I was there to improve my French. My study consisted of four hours of class work and four hours of homework. I was forbidden from reading, writing, speaking, or hearing English. I watched films in French, tried to read a story in *Le Monde** each day, listened to RFI* and a lot of Barbara* and Karim Oeullet*. At every meal I spoke French, and over the course of the seven weeks I felt myself gradually

15 losing touch with the broader world. This was not a wholly unpleasant feeling. In the moments I had to speak English (calling my wife, interacting with folks in town or at the book store), my mouth felt alien and my ear slightly off.

Acquiring a second language is hard. I have been told that it is easier for children, but I am not so sure if this is for reasons of biology or because adults have so much more to learn. Still, it remains true that

20 the vast majority of students at Middlebury were younger than me, and not just younger, but fiercer. My classmates were, in the main, the kind of high-achieving college students who elect to spend their summer vacation taking on eight hours a day of schoolwork. There was no difference in work ethic between us. If I spent more time studying than my classmates, that fact should not be taken as an accolade but as a marker of my inefficiency.

25 They had something over me, and that something was a culture, which is to say a suite of practices so ingrained as to be ritualistic. The scholastic* achievers knew how to quickly memorize a poem in a language they did not understand. They knew that recopying a handout a few days before an exam helped them digest the information. They knew to bring a pencil, not a pen, to that exam. They knew that you could (with the professor's permission) record lectures and take pictures of the blackboard.

30 This culture of scholastic achievement had not been acquired yesterday. The same set of practices had allowed my classmates to succeed in high school, and had likely been reinforced by other scholastic achievers around them. I am sure many of them had parents who were scholastic high-achievers. This is how social capital reinforces itself and compounds. It is not merely one high achieving child,

35 but a flock of high achieving children, each backed by high-achieving parents. I once talked to a woman who spoke German, English and French and had done so since she was a child. How did this happen, I asked? "Everyone in my world spoke multiple

40 languages," she explained. "It was just what you did."

> Glossary:
> *Le Monde* — a French newspaper
> RFI — Radio France Internationale, a French radio station
> Barbara — a French singer
> Karim Oeullet — a Canadian singer who sings in French
> scholastic — relating to school

Q1 Coates refers to childhood in this extract. What effect does this have?

....

....

....

....

....

....

Q2 You now need to refer only to lines 11-19.
How does the writer use language to describe learning French?

PAPER 2 Q3

Make some notes in the box, then write your answer on a separate piece of paper.

Q3 You now need to refer only to lines 20-32.
How does the writer use language to describe his classmates?

PAPER 2 Q3

Jot down some ideas in the box below, then write your answer on a separate piece of paper.

You can make a plan for any answer...

Even if it isn't the longest question, jotting down some ideas before you answer can help you to organise your ideas. This is especially handy if you're using evidence from different parts of the extract.

Exercise C — Comparing Texts

Q1 Compare how ideas about youth are presented in both extracts.

....

....

....

....

....

....

....

....

Q2 Compare how both writers convey their different perspectives and feelings about learning languages.

PAPER 2
Q4

Use the box below to make a plan, then write your answer on a separate piece of paper.

In your answer, you could:
- compare their different perspectives and feelings
- compare the methods the writers use to convey their different perspectives and feelings
- support your response with references to both texts.

Extension Activity

Both extracts talk about people picking up a new skill. Imagine you're organising an after-school club where students will be able to learn a new skill. Decide what the skill is going to be, then create a leaflet persuading students to join the club. Remember to use lots of persuasive devices.

WRITING
TASK

Practice Paper

This practice paper is similar in style to Section A of <u>Paper 2</u> of AQA GCSE English Language. To get the most out of these questions, read the sources and answer the questions as if you were actually in the exam. Give yourself <u>1 hour</u> to complete everything.

Exam Source A — How I Taught Myself Painting

This extract is from an article written by a writer named Crona Temple. In it, she describes learning to draw and paint. It was published in *The Girl's Own Paper*, a magazine aimed at young women, in 1882.

My home was in Donegal, the most north-westerly corner of Ireland; shut out by a savage mountain-range from all the rest of the world — fifty-six long Irish miles from a market-town, and thirty-six miles from a railway! I was fourteen years old before I ever set eyes on a railway, and I can remember now the feeling of shame that overwhelmed me when I was laughed at for a mistake I made
5   about our "iron roads." I had seen pictures of them, of course, and the rails were always drawn as long black lines; these I took for grooves, and very naturally concluded that the carriage-wheels ran along within them. When I noticed that the rails were *raised* that they stood up some inches from the ground, my astonishment was great. "How could the wheels be guided on those things?" I asked: and the innocent question drew down a storm of laughter that I have not forgotten to this day. I examined rails and wheels,
10   and solved the mystery for myself at the first place that we changed at; but the sore feeling remained in my heart for a long time.

I used to amuse myself in trying to make sketches of the scenery, but those wild moors and great bare hills made very bad subjects for a beginner's pencil. There were no old bridges and moss-grown bits of tree-trunk, no cottages with pointed roofs and rose-wreathed doors; only the wide mountains flecked with
15   cloud-shadows, and the wider Atlantic tumbling beneath its wall of cliff.

My "pictures" ended in vexation and sorrow. My eyes were more educated than my fingers; I could see my grievous failure, but how to make my hills look soft and far away, how to make my skies pure, and my water *like* water I did not know.

I was in despair. Painting, pencil-drawing even, was beyond my powers evidently.
20   But one day I was arranging a handful of bog-flowers in a glass saucer with some moss — butterworts they were, those lovely purple things that are worthy of a prettier name (I did not know their proper name then, and always called them "heath-stars"). Their bright, golden-green leaves shone like stars among the red and browns of the moss, and their graceful, slender flower-stems sprang from the centre in curves, which seemed but just strong enough to uphold the bit of brilliant colouring which the flower-petals gave.
25   I could not help trying to paint them, there and then.

I have that little drawing now. It is merely a childish scrawl; there is hardness in the hue of the blossoms, and a certain muddiness in the colouring of the leaves, but, in spite of all its faults, it has a truthfulness about it which is very pleasant to see.

From that day I attempted no more "pictures." I left the subtle beauties of sky and sea alone, and tried
30   to imitate the simpler beauty of the flowers, or the glossy wreaths of some ivy spray. If I failed in the *colouring*, the outline could at least be correct, and many a lesson of patience I learned over some tuft of thorny furze, or some long wand-like group of yellow iris.

And so time went on until I was about eighteen. My painting was not very grand, certainly, but it gave a great deal of pleasure to those whom I loved, and, if on that plea alone, it was not to be despised.
35   Even in that bleak land there were wonderful bits of beauty to educate my eyes and open my heart. The evening flush on the pearly hills baffled my ignorant fingers to copy, but I looked at it until its loveliness seemed to *sink into me*, and make me better and stronger. Some people learn *all* their lessons out of bound books; I wonder if they have an idea that lessons learned out of doors are just as valuable, and a vast deal pleasanter! Let them love their books as much as they choose, but I would say to them,
40   "Glance into God's book of Nature — study the flowers and the birds, and the way the great trees grow, and see if you are not astonished and made better by what you learn there."

Exam Source B — My apple's not perfect, but this art class has appeal

The following text comes from a review written by Harry Mount, published in *The Daily Mail* in 2021. In it, Mount describes his experience attending an art class to learn how to paint.

Not since 1985 have I put paintbrush to canvas. That was when my long-suffering art teacher at school, Miss Miller, politely agreed with me that I shouldn't do art O-level*.

Fast-forward to 2021 and I'm tempted to make up for lost time — but what good could a course in Old Master painting techniques do for a talentless, out-of-practice hack like me?

5   Quite a lot, I discover. Painting is something we come to appreciate more as we get older. In the same way that I wasn't interested in gardening or birdsong when I was a teenager (and now love both), it takes middle age to appreciate the pleasure of restful contemplation of the outside world. Even if your art is rubbish — like mine.

So off I went to The Bell, a 16th-century palace of a pub in Ticehurst, East Sussex, for a one-day course.
10   Nine of us pupils took over a huge, well-lit room there for a day.

Our teacher was artist Dani Humberstone, until recently vice-president of the Society of Women Artists. She gave an invigorating crash course in oil painting to me and my fellow apprentices: eight friendly ladies — all much better painters than me, though they were too charmingly modest to say so.

For those in the class who had been painting on their own, this was their opportunity for their artistic
15   skills to take a leap forward.

First, she taught us how to draw an outline of a Royal Gala apple on a canvas board. I divided my board into quarters with a chalk pencil so that I had a sense of scale.

Then I learnt the technique perfected by baroque artist Caravaggio: chiaroscuro — Italian for 'light-dark' — where you produce strong contrasts between brightness and shade.

20   You may not see much chiaroscuro in my apple. But Dani ingeniously showed us how to produce a three-dimensional look by painting dark shadows on one side of the apple, and adding dashes of white highlights on the other.

By making the middle of the apple light and both sides darker, you 'pull' the fruit out of the canvas, bulging towards the viewer, to give the illusion of 3D reality.

25   Dani has exhibited at the Royal Academy and the Florence Biennale. It must have been a bit of a comedown to address the shortcomings of my still life. But she was endlessly encouraging.

'There's a lot to be said for looking naive,' she said, when my apple stayed resolutely flat and refused to jump into the third dimension.

At other times, she bolstered the class by crying, 'Think Leonardo da Vinci — take out your brush
30   marks!'

We got a deep immersion in paint — and not just the burnt umber (reddish-brown) colour I splashed all over my shirt. Do wear old clothes for the course.

I was transfixed by trying — and failing — to get my apple right. But I didn't mind the failure. For the first time in months, I was transported to a different universe, where I never felt the need to look at my
35   cursed phone once.

Text continues on the next page

Jane McWilliam, an osteopath from Burgess Hill, West Sussex, agreed. An accomplished artist — her glowing apple painting was a lesson in chiaroscuro — she revels in the release painting brings. 'It's an escape from shopping lists, working, getting somewhere on time, intense living,' she said. 'It's time out from the diary routine.'

40 My fellow pupils were kind about my efforts. But, as you can see from the apple I painted from 10am to 3.30pm, the art world can rest easy. I am no late-flowering genius. That's the point. The class caters for all talents.

Among my group was Denise Fisk, a professional artist from nearby Crowborough. 'You don't think about anything else when you're painting,' she told me. 'All your mind is thinking of is colour, form and 45 paint. You're giving your brain a rest from yourself.'

I couldn't have agreed more as I sat next to the inglenook* at The Bell, admiring my painting.

Glossary
* O-level — a secondary school qualification that was replaced by GCSEs.
* inglenook — a type of large fireplace

SECTION A: Reading

Q1 Read again the first part of **Source A** from **lines 1 to 11**.

Choose **four** statements below which are **true**.

- Shade the **circles** in the boxes of the ones that you think are **true**.
- Choose a maximum of **four** statements.
- If you make an error cross out the **whole box**.
- If you change your mind and require a statement that has been crossed out then draw a circle around the box.

[4 marks]

A	Crona Temple is from north east Ireland.	○
B	Crona Temple lived in an isolated part of Ireland.	○
C	Crona Temple's home was next to a railway.	○
D	Crona Temple first saw a picture of a railway when she was fourteen.	○
E	Crona Temple was laughed at for calling the railways "iron roads".	○
F	Crona Temple was surprised that the rails weren't embedded in the ground.	○
G	Crona Temple was interested in how railways worked.	○
H	Crona Temple was upset for a long time about people laughing at her.	○

Q2   You need to refer to **Source A** and **Source B** for this question.

Both writers try to learn a new skill.

Use details from **both** sources to write a summary of what you understand
about the differences between how the writers learn new skills.

[8 marks]

....

....

....

....

....

....

....

....

....

....

....

....

....

....

....

....

....

....

....

....

....

....

....

....

Q3 You now need to refer only to **Source A** from **lines 20 to 32**.

How does the writer use language to describe the flowers?

[12 marks]

....

....

....

....

....

....

....

....

....

....

....

....

....

....

....

....

....

....

....

....

....

....

....

Q4 For this question, you need to refer to the **whole of Source A**, together with the **whole of Source B**.

Compare how the writers convey their different perspectives and feelings about creating art.

In your answer, you could:

- compare their different perspectives and feelings about creating art
- compare the methods they use to convey their different perspectives and feelings
- support your ideas with references to both texts.

[16 marks]

....

....

....

....

....

....

....

....

....

....

....

....

....

....

....

....

....

....

....

....

....

....

....

....

....

....

....

....

....

....

....

....

....

....

....

....

....

....

....

....

....

....

....

....

....
....
....
....
....
....
....
....
....
....
....
....
....
....
....
....
....
....
....
....
....
....
....
....
....
....
....
....

Answers

Section One — Australian Adventures

Pages 2-4: Exercise A — Down Under

1. a) Any three words or phrases about the uninhabited landscape from the correct part of the extract. Answers might include:
   - "barren"
   - "a lonely mailbox"
   - "the only other lively thing"

   b) You might have said Bryson felt uncomfortable because he uses a simile to compare the journey to spending "the day in a cement mixer". This implies that it was an unpleasant and physically painful experience for him.

   Don't worry if you've talked about a different feeling to the one above — just make sure that you've used evidence from the text to support your view.

2. You should have given an example from the text that suggests that living in White Cliffs would be difficult and then explained how it gives you this impression. For example:
   - Bryson describes White Cliffs as "a listless world of heat and dust." You might have commented on the adjective "listless", which evokes a sense of lifelessness, or the use of "world of", which highlights how the entirety of White Cliffs appears to be made up of heat and dust. This shows how difficult it might be to thrive there.
   - Bryson likens living in White Cliffs to colonizing Mars, stating how you'd need the same "tolerance and fortitude" to live in either. This analogy suggests that life there would be difficult, and makes it seem alien and other-worldly.

3. Any two ideas or descriptions from the correct part of the extract that show the appeal of White Cliffs, followed by a brief explanation of why they have this effect. For example:
   - The description of the "Kangaroos... grazing picturesquely" is appealing because it creates a romantic image of nature that might seem quite exotic to readers outside of Australia.
   - The incredible view, where there isn't "a scrap of intrusion" for forty miles, makes White Cliffs seems very peaceful. You could add that as there isn't even "a scrap" of anything interrupting the view, it highlights this sense of tranquillity.

4. a) Any three examples from the extract which relate to colour. Answers might include:
   - "a coating of red dust"
   - "a small blotch"
   - "the two bleached hills"
   - "colour in a hundred layered shades"
   - "glowing pinks"
   - "deep purples"
   - "careless banners of pure crimson"

   b) You should have talked about how Bryson uses colour to give you an initial idea of White Cliffs and the surrounding area, then how he uses colour to challenge this idea later in the extract. Here are some things you could have mentioned:
   - Bryson describes how they were coated in "red dust" on their journey. Red is often associated with aggression or warning signs, which implies there may be danger ahead.
   - The lack of colour in the "bleached hills" makes White Cliffs seem bleak, as though whatever colour was once there has been removed by the harsh environment.
   - The sunset at the end of the extract fills the landscape with colour "in a hundred layered shades". The use of "layered" hints that there's a level of depth to White Cliffs that was previously hidden.
   - The listing of colours, such as "glowing pinks, deep purples" etc. makes White Cliffs seem vibrant and full compared to earlier in the extract, reflecting how Bryson's opinion of White Cliffs has started to change.

5. All your points should use relevant examples from lines 13-21, use relevant terminology, and comment on the effects of the language used. Here are some things you could have mentioned:
   - The use of the simile "like stepping into an early James Bond movie" suggests that the motel looks stylish and that Bryson is impressed by his surroundings.
   - Bryson calls the houses "dwellings" and describes them as being "burrowed" into the hills. These words have connotations of animal habitats, suggesting that the houses are rustic.

- Adjectives like "cavelike" and "windowless" suggest that Bryson finds the rooms somewhat disconcerting, despite his earlier assertion that they are "very nice and quite normal". This is reinforced by the "darkness and silence" which makes the rooms sound almost menacing.

Pages 5-6: Exercise B — Letters from Australia

You should have ticked B, D, E and F only.

2. You should have talked about the impression you get from this part of the extract and explained why. For example:
   - The journey seems dull and uninspiring. The writer describes circular sailing as "tedious" and "very monotonous". The use of the adverb "very" emphasises how boring the writer finds this type of sailing.
   - The journey seems to be going smoothly for the writer and his brother. The writer says that there has been "very little to trouble" them and they have a "very clever captain". This alliteration emphasises the adjective "clever", and shows the captain is in control of the ship.

3. You should have said how the second letter presents a different impression of the brothers' experience. Here are some things you could have mentioned:
   - The second letter makes life in Australia sound tough compared to the ship. The image of "1000 or 1500 more tents" that are "exposed to wind and weather" creates a dismal impression. The verb "exposed" highlights how these people are vulnerable and have no protection.
   - The structure of the second letter highlights how there is a lot more happening. Splitting the letter into sections about Australia's employment, weather and a description of Melbourne shows how much there is to talk about.
   - The second letter adopts a more narrative style, making the brothers' experience seem more interesting. For example, the simile used to describe the dust "like a mist, with swarms of sand flies which injure the eyes" makes even the uncomfortable aspects sound interesting.

4. Your answer will depend on how you interpret the letters, but you should have backed up whatever you've said with evidence. Here are some things you could have mentioned:
   - Herbert seems more reserved than his brother Henry. He uses less detailed language, such as "very exciting", while Henry uses more descriptive language, such as "myriads of arrivals", to describe their travels. Herbert also leaves most of the writing for Henry to do.
   - Henry seems more emotional and animated. He uses exclamations ("none to be had!") and wishes his family well at the end of his letter. On the other hand, Herbert signs off his letter with "Can't think of anything more at present", showing him to be calmer and less emotive.

Page 7: Exercise C — Comparing Texts

1. You should have compared the writers' attitudes in detail, using relevant examples and terminology to support your points. Here are some things you could have mentioned:
   - The Humphrey brothers seem to have a more optimistic attitude to Australia. They describe it as a place where one "can make his fortune in a few years". The use of "few" emphasises how little time it takes, which emphasises the idea that Australia is a land of opportunity. In contrast, Bryson says that the Australian desert is "as barren an expanse" as he had ever seen. The adjective "barren" creates the impression that it is an unfruitful place that can't support life. This suggests that Bryson views Australia more negatively than the Humphrey brothers.
   - Both extracts end by focusing on favourable attitudes to Australia. Bryson considers the lingering beauty of White Cliffs and concludes by directly quoting a resident of White Cliffs, who says they'd "find these sunsets hard to give up". This makes the beauty of White Cliffs sound addicting and emphasises how spectacular they are. Henry Humphrey says that they have made "no sacrifice" and are "saving money" in Melbourne. This implies that the brothers are prospering, ending with a positive attitude towards what Australia has to offer.

2. You should have summarised the differences between the two places, using quotations and inferences to support your points. Here are some things you could have mentioned:
   - Melbourne is shown to be a place where people go in hopes of "bettering" their "condition". The use of "bettering" implies that one can improve themselves in Melbourne, making it sound like a good place to live. However, the people in White Cliffs are said to need "tolerance" and "fortitude" to stay, which suggests life there is difficult and isn't somewhere most people would choose to move to.
   - Bryson makes White Cliffs seem empty. He uses language associated with isolation, such as "barren" and "lonely" to create the impression that there is nothing or nobody there. In contrast, Melbourne is described as a busy place. The mention of "1000 or 1500 more tents" shows the large number of people in contrast to White Cliffs. It is said to be "a healthy place" with "some good shops". The adjective "healthy" suggests that it is in good condition and functioning well as a city.

You could also compare the "healthy" Melbourne with the lifeless White Cliffs, which is described as a "listless world of heat and dust".

Section Two — Teaching in Prisons

Pages 8-10: Exercise A —
Some Eminent Women of Our Times

1. You should have ticked boxes C, D, E and G only.
2. a) Direct address.
   b) You should have talked about the effect direct address has on the reader. Here are some things you could have mentioned:
      - It involves the reader in the text and encourages them to care about the social issues that are described. The writer isn't just giving the reader information, it is as though she is talking to them.
      - The phrase "Every one of us" groups readers together with the writer. The collective pronoun "us" creates a feeling of unity. You could have added that this makes it more likely the reader will empathise with Fawcett's opinions.
3. a) You should have said that it means the prisoners' sense of right and wrong / how good or bad their behaviour is.
   b) You should have talked about the effect the description of the woman has on you as a reader. Here are some things you could have mentioned:
      - It creates sympathy because the woman is presented as an unfortunate victim of circumstance. The adjective "poor" suggests misfortune as well as poverty, and this effectively encourages the reader to feel sorry for her.
      - The noun "creature" dehumanises the woman, implying that if she is not human, she might not understand how she should behave. You could have added that this might make the reader pity her because if she's just a "creature", it might be that she didn't know how to love her child.
4. You should have talked about how Sarah Martin saw that there was nothing to aid the development of prisoners (there was no school, chaplain or religious services), that she didn't feel comfortable visiting the prison at first and that her first meeting with a prisoner was an emotional experience.

You could have mentioned that Sarah Martin was unsuccessful the first time she tried to visit the prison.

5. You should have talked about how the extract has been structured to interest you as a reader. Here are some things you could have mentioned:
   - Fawcett starts by introducing the key moral message behind the story that follows. By stating how "neither leisure nor wealth are necessary" to improve the world, she foreshadows the poverty mentioned later and prepares the reader for the subject matter of the extract.
   - Fawcett tells the story of Sarah Martin in chronological order. You could have talked about how phrases such as "When", "She was first" and "From" mark and show the passage of time. This guides the reader through the story and helps them see how things developed for Martin.

- The "deeply religious" nature of Sarah Martin is emphasised through the structure of the extract. The lack of religious "services" is mentioned in both the third and the final paragraph. This repetition highlights how important religion was to Sarah Martin and involves the reader by helping them to understand her motivation. This makes the reader more likely to care about Martin's work.

6. You should have agreed or disagreed with the statement and given reasons to support and explain your view.
   If you agreed with the statement, you could have mentioned:
   - The writer describes Sarah Martin's character very positively, and her actions as "extraordinary". Describing Martin's "native goodness of heart" shows that the writer admires her ability to help others in spite of her own poverty. You could have added that the adjective "native" implies that it is a key part of Martin's character, which emphasises the writer's admiration of her.
   - The writer references religion several times and goes on to say that Martin was the first person to introduce religious services at the prison. This gives the impression that Sarah Martin is doing good and holy work. You could add that using words associated with religion such as "tempted", "Satan" and "wickedness" emphasises the difficulty Martin faced bringing God into the prisoners' lives, which highlights how the writer admires her efforts for doing so.
   If you disagreed, you could have mentioned:
   - As her book was intended to inspire good work, Fawcett would have hoped that her positive descriptions of Sarah Martin's behaviour would encourage young readers to follow her example and do similar good work. This means that a reader could view the descriptions as being exaggerated to emphasise Martin's positive attributes, rather than showing sincere admiration.

Remember, it doesn't matter whether you agree or disagree, as long as you can support your opinion with evidence from the extract.

Pages 11-12: Exercise B — Secret Teacher

1. A wide range or great variety of different problems.
2. You should have said why you think the article was written anonymously. Here are some things you could have mentioned:
   - The article features sensitive topics such as "rehab", the prisoners' "criminality" and "drug abuse". These topics make it likely that the writer wants to keep their identity, and that of the prisoners, private.
   - The writer might be trying to protect his students and stop them from being ashamed that they didn't finish school properly. As the prisoners in the extract are adults, they might be embarrassed that they have the "reading levels" of "teenagers" and don't have "entry level" academic qualifications.

The use of pronouns like "he" and "him" alongside descriptive names such as "A learner" and "a man in his 50s" emphasise the writer's desire for privacy.

3. You should have described the tone of the extract and explained how it has been created. For example:
   - The tone is quite matter-of-fact. The writer uses a simple, blunt statement to open the paragraph — "These men require sensitive handling." The direct tone helps the author talk about difficult topics honestly and convey key information to the reader in a straightforward way.
   - The tone is personal at times. The writer mentions their own life and thoughts ("It was a revelation to me") and this helps the reader empathise with them. They also imply that working in the prison affected them as a person when they describe some of their students as "memorable", showing how their students had a long-lasting impact upon them. By referring to working "together one-on-one", they suggest that they built a connection and a bond with the prisoners.

Answers

4.	All your points should use relevant examples from lines 15-29, use relevant terminology, and comment on the effects of the language used to describe the prisoners. Here are some things you could have mentioned:
- Listing the prisoners' personal problems in lines 15-16 ("Custody issues, homelessness, bullying, debt, addiction, poverty, loneliness, alcoholism, abuse, self-harm") creates an almost overwhelming sense of suffering. This emphasises the writer's sadness at everything the prisoners have experienced and encourages the reader to feel the same.
- Sympathetic language is used to describe the tragically limited development of the prisoners. They are described as "frightened, abused, lonely and unloved boys". These emotive adjectives encourage the reader to empathise with their struggles.
- The use of parenthesis around the word "calmer" slows the pace of the text. This encourages the reader to slow down and reflect on the prisoner's change in attitude, so they are left with the impression that those in prison are capable of change.

Page 13: Exercise C — Comparing Texts

1.	You should have used examples from both extracts to make comparisons between how the writers create sympathy for the prisoners. Here are some things you could have mentioned:
- Fawcett dehumanises prisoners to create sympathy, whereas the writer of Extract B encourages readers to connect with the prisoners on a personal level. Fawcett refers to one of the prisoners as a "poor creature", which makes the reader think more about a victimised animal than it does about a human who's done something terrible. In contrast, the writer of Extract B says that while many people have a negative opinion of prisoners, they are actually "just like everyone else". This helps to create a connection between the prisoners and the reader, and enables the reader to have a greater understanding of their situation.
- Both writers present changes in the prisoners' attitudes to create a sympathetic response. Fawcett describes how the prisoner Martin first visited was "rough" at first, but later "burst into tears" and expressed how she wanted help "to be a better woman". Similarly, the writer of Extract B recalls a student who changed from a "thuggish brute" to "one of the most dedicated learners" they'd had. The effect of these 'character arcs' is that prisoners are seen less as terrible human beings, and more like misunderstood people who need to be given time and support. This helps the reader to see the prisoners in the same way the teachers do.
2.	You should have summarised the similar experiences in each text, using quotations and inferences to support points. Here are some things you could have mentioned:
- Both writers present teaching in prisons as a rewarding experience. Fawcett mentions how the prisoner's "gratitude" on Martin's first visit inspired Martin to devote her "best energies" to working there — this suggests that she found the experience valuable. The writer of extract B describes how "it's so satisfying" when prisoners start to "trust" you and what you teach. The writer uses the adverb "so" to emphasise just how "satisfying" they found teaching there, which suggests the experience also benefits teachers.
- In both texts, the prisoners are initially unwelcoming towards their teachers, but this relationship improves. Fawcett describes the "rough" speech of the prisoner when Sarah Martin first meets her, implying that she does not welcome Martin, but the prisoner comes to accept Martin's "deep compassion". Similarly, the writer of Extract B is at first sworn at by a prisoner ("reeled off a load of expletives"), but in time this "thuggish brute" becomes a "dedicated" learner. This shows that teaching in prisons can have a powerful impact on the prisoners.

Section Three — Musical Matters

Pages 14-16: Exercise A — He Knows the Score

1.	You should have ticked boxes A, D, F and G only.
2.	You should have talked about how it tells you John Williams shot to fame very quickly. Meteors fly swiftly through space, so comparing Williams to one implies that he rapidly became famous and reached "the big-time".
3. a)	Any two language techniques from the correct part of the extract, followed by a brief explanation of what effect they have. For example:
- Williams uses lists to build up the description of his music. These lists cause the description to gain momentum and create the feeling of a growing presence, much like the shark in the film the music will accompany.
- Ellipses are used to show where Williams pauses in his description. You could have said that these pauses build suspense and make the reader anticipate what is coming next, or that they reflect how Williams is almost composing the music in his head, pausing to think what he'll do next.
- Direct address ("You see") makes Williams's description seem aimed at the reader. This makes the tone seem lighter and more conversational, which engages the reader by making it feel like Williams is speaking to them.
   b)	You should have given another example of Williams describing music in the extract and explained the effect it had on you. Here are some things you could have mentioned:
- The 'Close Encounters of the Third Kind' music is described as a seed that grows in the mind of the audience whether they know it or not. This highlights the complexity of Williams's compositions by showing the reader how they can grow, develop, and have very subtle effects on people.
- Williams describes the music from 'Close Encounters of the Third Kind' as creating a "sense of recognition" that is "spiritual" and "fulfilling". This suggests that music can create an enriching experience and encourages the reader to appreciate how composers "evolve a score" as a film progresses.
4. a)	You could have talked about how delaying the reveal of Williams's success emphasises how far he has come since he first pitched his 'Jaws' music ideas to a nervous Steven Spielberg, or how it lets the reader form their own opinion of Williams before they find out about his incredible success.
   b)	You should have said whether you think the extract is / isn't structured as you would expect an interview to be and used relevant examples to support your view.
   If it is structured as you'd expect, you might have mentioned:
- There are lots of direct quotes from John Williams throughout the extract. This is typical of an interview because it not only lets the reader learn the subject's opinions first hand, but it gives the interview a structure that is more reflective of a conversation.
   If it isn't, you might have mentioned:
- In the extract, questions and answers aren't presented in turn. The Q&A structure is probably the most common for interviews because it mirrors the conversation that takes place between the interviewer and interviewee, giving the reader the sense that they are sat there with them.
- The extract contains the opinions of the interviewer. This is not common in interviews because the reader is likely to be more interested in the thoughts of the person being interviewed. You could have added that this gives the extract a more narrative style than you'd expect in a more typical interview.
5.	You should have talked about how the relationship between music and film is presented in the final paragraph. Here are some things you could have mentioned:
- The writer says that "Movie music is made to measure, not sold by the yard". This makes the reader think about a tailor, which highlights how each film score is original rather than being mass produced. The use of language related to fashion emphasises how film music is carefully crafted to each individual piece of cinema, much like a tailor would make or adjust a garment to suit one specific individual.

Answers

- The writer uses the metaphor of music being more than just "aural grouting" to highlight how music and film complement each other, rather than music simply filling in the gaps. Music is described as "inseparable" from the film 'Close Encounters of the Third Kind', emphasising how interconnected the two kinds of media are.
- Emotive language is used to highlight how significant music is to the enjoyment of cinema when used correctly. The phrase "it's at the very heart of the movie" emphasises the significance of film music and implies that it could even be the most important part of a film. The intensifying adverb "very" shows how strongly the writer holds this view.

Pages 17-18: Exercise B — George Eliot's Journal

1. a) Any two relevant ideas from the correct part of the extract. For example:
   - Music can bring people together in mutual appreciation.
   - Music can make people feel emotional.
   - Music can be heart-warming / make people feel good.
   b) You should have talked about an example where Eliot uses language to make the music seem attractive and inviting. Here are some things you could have mentioned:
   - Eliot uses the exclamation "How the music warmed one's heart!" to make the music seem appealing and emphasise how moving it was. The possessive pronoun "one's" makes this even more engaging for the reader, as it's more inclusive than if Eliot has used 'my' instead.
   - The music is described as irresistible. By referring to the "delicious sound" of the organ, Eliot implies that it is too tempting to be ignored. Using an adjective usually associated with eating makes the music seems even more appealing, as though her ears are hungry to consume as much of it as they can.
2. You should have agreed or disagreed with the statement and used relevant examples from the extract to support and explain your view. If you agreed with the statement, you could have mentioned:
   - The paragraph is structured chronologically. Phrases such as "Coming back from", "then we reached", and "drew us farther and farther in" guide the reader through Eliot's experience alongside her. This immerses the reader in the text and makes the events described feel more real.
   - In the paragraph, Eliot keeps shifting her focus from where she moved ("we reached the market-place"), what she saw ("a full view") and what she heard ("We heard the organ"). This structure constantly keeps the reader's senses engaged, bringing her time in Nürnberg to life in a more vivid way and helping them to imagine that they are walking through the streets with her.

Don't worry if you disagreed with the statement — just make sure that you can support your view with relevant evidence from the text.

3. All your points should use relevant examples from lines 4-12, use relevant terminology and comment on the effect of the language used to describe Nürnberg. Here are some things you could have mentioned:
   - Eliot uses a list of colours and repeats the word "or" ("delicate green, or buff, or pink, or lilac"), emphasising that the colours of Nürnberg are varied and overwhelming.
   - Eliot uses personification to bring the houses to life by describing them with words which are usually associated with descriptions of people ("neighbor", "physiognomy", "family likeness"). This gives the impression that the houses all have unique appearances, just like people do.
   - Eliot juxtaposes how she imagined Nürnberg to be before her visit with the "reality" of the city. She thought the town would have "narrow streets" and be "dark" and "sombre", but discovers it is "bright" and colourful. The sharp contrast between light and dark imagery helps to emphasise the city's true beauty.

Page 19: Exercise C — Comparing Texts

1. You should have used relevant examples from both extracts to make comparisons between their style and tone. Here are some things you could have mentioned:
   - Williams is a professional composer and the extract reflects this with a more formal style. The writer uses technical language such as "ostinato" and "semitone" to explore the topic of composing music. Extract B is written in a much more personal style. Eliot is recording her personal experience of Nürnberg and so examines even the smallest details, such as the baby having "Such a funny little complete face". This emphasises how much more relaxed Eliot's style is.
   - Extract A is an interview and is intended to inform readers, so the style is adapted to present different forms of information clearly. First person quotes from Williams are clearly marked with phrases like "Williams explains:" so that the reader knows when they are reading Williams's own words. Extract B is a personal journal and so was likely written without an audience in mind. The detailed descriptions, like "an exquisite bit of florid Gothic", are probably more likely included to help Eliot remember her experience in the future rather than to inform others.
2. You should have compared the writers' similar attitudes to music in detail, using relevant examples and terminology to support your points. Here are some things you could have mentioned:
   - Both writers believe that music can have a strong effect on people. When discussing the music for the film 'Close Encounters of the Third Kind', Williams uses natural imagery to explain how he wanted to plant just five notes "in the minds of the audience" and watch how these "thematic seeds" grew into a "fulfilling" climax. Using just five notes emphasises how such a simple piece of music can have a big effect if used in the right way. Similarly, in Extract B, Eliot describes the "stream of listening people" following a marching band. By using the metaphor of the stream, Eliot creates an image of a continuous crowd of people trailing the musicians, emphasising their power over an audience.
   - Both writers believe that music can contribute to an atmosphere. Williams considers music to be "a good dramatic device", which is used in 'Jaws' to create "the suspense of the film". This shows that Williams thinks music is important in building the film's tense atmosphere for the viewers. Similarly, the organ music that Eliot hears in the church causes her to feel "devout emotions" and "blends everything into harmony". This suggests that the beautiful sound of the music contributes to a peaceful, reverent atmosphere inside the church.

Section Four — Messing About on Boats

Pages 20-22: Exercise A — Following the Equator

1. a) You should have said how you think Mark Twain feels at this point in the extract, using an example to support your view. For example:
   - Mark Twain seems excited to set sail. The phrase "at last" suggests he was eager and happy to depart.
   - Mark Twain seems short of patience. He describes his journey across America as "a snail-paced march", which suggests it was tediously slow.
   b) You should have explained how the first paragraph being one line long contributes to the feeling you mentioned in part a). For example:
   - The way Twain moves quickly on to describing the journey across the sea emphasises his excitement to set sail. It's as though he can't wait to tell the reader about it.
   - It mirrors the shortness of Twain's patience — it's almost as though he doesn't want to spend any more time describing setting sail, he'd rather move on to something new.
2. a) You should have given a linguistic device Twain uses in this part of the extract and explained its effect. For example:
   - He uses listing in his description of the sea. This emphasises the size of the sea and shows the reader how captivated Twain is by the water because he has so much to say about it.
   - He uses repetition to help his readers imagine the ocean. Repeating the 'ee' sound in "sea", "me" and "weeks" creates a rhythm that mimics the waves which "rippled" continually against the ship as it sailed.

Answers

- He uses alliteration in phrases like "sparkling summer sea" and "clean and cool sea". The soft 's' sound emphasises how relaxing Twain finds the ocean, while the harder 'c' sound reflects the ship cutting through the water as it sails.

b) You should have said something about how Twain thinks he overpaid for the chairs. By saying they cost as much as "honest chairs", Twain thinks he was deceived when he bought them because they were not of good quality.

c) You should have talked about the impression you get of Twain from the second paragraph and explained why. Here are some things you could have mentioned:
- Mark Twain enjoys the relaxed nature of sea travel. He considers the journey a "holiday" in which he has "nothing to do but do nothing and be comfortable". The repetition of "nothing" emphasises how much leisure time he has.
- Twain seems to take pride in himself and how he presents himself to others. For example, he feels "shame" when his chair collapses beneath him in front of "all the passengers", which suggests he cares about how other people see him.
- He appears to have a sense of humour. Twain exaggerates the hardship faced by those who had to "go without" their own deck-chair by hyperbolically comparing such a situation to the "Dark Ages". This entertains the reader and encourages them to appreciate Twain's personality more.

3. You should have said something about how while the food or ingredients were good, the chef was not. The word "furnished" can mean 'provided', so it means that the food was provided by God ("the Deity"). The contrast between the "Deity" and the "devil" shows how bad the cooking was because it turned something heavenly into something hellish.

4. All your points should use relevant examples from lines 18-34, use relevant terminology, and comment on the effects of the language used to describe the captain. Here are some things you could have mentioned:
- The captain is described as "a very handsome man, tall and perfectly formed". This description gives the impression that the captain is a good-looking man because he is well-built and physically attractive.
- The captain's voice is described as "sweet", and he is said to use it "with taste and effect". This implies that he is a good singer and that he uses his voice well to entertain the passengers on the boat.
- Twain states that the captain only enforces the rule about there being no lights in the smoking room after eleven "and one other" rule, despite there being "many laws on the ship's statute book". The makes the captain seem like a relaxed, easygoing person, and this willingness to ignore some rules shows he is not a strict leader.
- He is described as having "the best intentions" and a "soft grace and finish" to his behaviour. This makes the captain seem kind and thoughtful. This implies that he tries to avoid causing other people upset where possible and creates a favourable impression of the captain.

You could have talked about how "grace" is sometimes used to mean the favour or approval of God, and how this makes the captain seem like a good, kind and religious man.

Pages 23-24: Exercise B — Smoke on the Water

1. You should have given an example from the text that shows the writer enjoys the French countryside and then explained how it gives you this impression. For example:
- The view from the boat is described as "absurdly pretty scenery". The adverb "absurdly" emphasises how beautiful the writer finds the view — it is almost beyond belief. This reveals how incredible she thinks the countryside is.
- The writer describes the scene around the boat as a "nature reserve", and says that the water is "serene". This suggests it is an area of great natural beauty, and the adjective "serene" creates the impression of deep peacefulness and calm, implying that the writer takes pleasure in how quiet and relaxing the countryside is.

- The cornfields which line the water are described as "golden". This suggests that the corn glistens like gold in the sunlight, making nature seem beautiful as well as valuable and precious.

2. You should have talked about how the tone of the extract changes in the last four paragraphs, explaining how the change occurs and what effect it has. Here are some things you could have mentioned:
- The tone is one of relaxation in lines 20-21, with the use of the verbs "lying" and "resting", and the adverb "casually", suggesting that the family feel comfortable and confident on the boat.
- There is an abrupt shift in tone in line 29. The phrase "Then it happens" creates a feeling of fear and apprehension because it isn't clear what happened. The tone then becomes more panicked with the exclamation "Turn the engine off!" and this sudden shout from the writer emphasises how worried she feels.

3. All your points should use relevant examples from lines 8-19, use relevant terminology, and comment on the effects of the language used to describe learning to drive a boat. Here are some things you could have mentioned:
- The writer asks a rhetorical question, "What could possibly go wrong?", to create a comical sense of foreboding that something bad will happen. This suggests that the writer thinks that learning to drive a boat will be beyond her capabilities.
- The writer creates a contrast between how her family looks and how the other families look. Whereas the other families are "relaxed and jolly", the writer's family look like they are there "by mistake". This juxtaposition suggests that the writer feels unprepared to drive a boat.
- The writer uses several energetic verbs to describe the tasks involved with driving a boat ("grab", "pull", "lasso", "leap"). These verbs make the process of learning how to drive a boat sound strenuous and exhausting.

Page 25: Exercise C — Comparing Texts

1. You should have compared the methods each writer uses to entertain their audience and explained their effects. Here are some things you could have mentioned:
- Twain's language is playful, such as in phrases like "nothing to do but do nothing" where the repetition gives the text a humorous and whimsical feel. His dryly comic description of the "over-supply of cockroaches" on the ship demonstrates his joking attitude towards his surroundings, providing an entertaining account of less positive aspects of his journey.
- Cook uses humour and hyperbole to establish a comic tone in the extract. She writes that her child "threw up" during a ferry crossing and how a separate boat journey involved "more vomiting". These blunt descriptions create humour, making the text entertaining for the reader. Later in the extract, Cook dramatically compares her minor boat malfunction to a kind of military emergency, describing how "Red lights flash from every dial". These humorous and hyperbolic descriptions make the account of the Cook family's experience on boats entertaining for the reader.

2. You should have used relevant examples from both extracts to compare the writers' different attitudes to travelling by boat. Here are some things you could have mentioned:
- Mark Twain finds the experience more relaxing than Emma Cook. Twain describes himself as feeling "contented and at peace" on the ship, and focuses on the on-board entertainment such as the "good food", "singing" and "piano playing". This emphasises how comfortable Twain is on the boat. On the other hand, Cook has a more hands-on experience, describing an "introductory lesson" and how she had to "negotiate locks". The use of "negotiate" shows a certain level of effort and suggests that Cook felt unable to completely relax. This implies she found travelling by boat less peaceful than Twain.

Answers

- Twain has a more realistic attitude to travelling by boat than Cook. Twain accepts that there will be problems when travelling long distances at sea in "the tropics", such as "discipline" issues and "an over-supply of cockroaches". This practical attitude shows the reader that Twain is able to accept both the positives and negatives of travelling by boat and appreciate the experience as a whole. In contrast, Cook's description of travelling by boat reveals a more unrealistic attitude. She varies from perfect "picturesque canals" to chaos as "An alarm that pierces the silence" begins blaring. This demonstrates how her idyllic vision of travelling by boat doesn't match up to the more turbulent reality she experiences.

You could have talked about how each writers' role on their boats affects their attitude — Twain was a passenger while Cook was her own 'crew'.

Section Five — Homelessness in History

Pages 26-28: Exercise A — The Story of Hooverville in Seattle

1. a) You should have identified the purpose of the extract and then explained your reasoning. For example:
   - You could have said that the purpose of the extract is to inform readers about how the Hooverville came to be. Jackson creates a detailed, chronological account of his experiences from his time being "registered at a Central Registry" to when Hooverville earned its name, carefully recounting the "difficulties" he faced along the way.
   - You might have said that the purpose of the extract is to persuade the reader to sympathise with his cause. Jackson infuses his writing with his opinions and frequently refers to his "suffering", using emotive language and his personal viewpoint to influence and persuade the reader.
   b) Your answer here will depend on your answer to part a), but you should have explained how you think this information aids the purpose of the text. For example:
   - If you thought that the purpose was to inform, the inclusion of this detail might make the reader trust the writer's view more. This would make the extract seem more reliable.
   - If you thought that the purpose was to persuade, this information might make the reader sympathise with Jackson more. This might make them more receptive to his account.

2. a) Any three facts about the Central Registry, either paraphrased or directly quoted, from the correct part of the extract. Answers might include:
   - The food resembled "pig swill".
   - They were given "no morning or noonday meal".
   - The floors they slept on were hard.
   - They used newspapers they had found to make their beds.
   b) You should have talked about how Jackson felt angry or disappointed about his treatment, using evidence to show how he conveys this to the reader. Here are some things you could have mentioned:
   - Jackson describes the food he received as more similar to "pig swill" than "human food". This analogy suggests that Jackson felt as though the men at the Central Registry were being treated like animals, with the authorities not really concerned about the standard of their care and welfare.
   - He frequently uses negative language in this part of the extract ("no", "few", "hard", "bitter realities"). This builds a detailed, negative impression of the Central Registry and emphasises the tough conditions and hardship he endured.
   c) You should have talked about how Jackson implies that his time with the other homeless people was more positive than his time at the Central Registry, and then explained how he gives you this impression. Here are some things you could have mentioned:
   - Jackson talks about how they "immediately set in" constructing their "shacks" and devising a system for their "shanty town". This implies a sense of productivity that he never experienced at the Central Registry.
   - He says they began to "construct and work out a relief system" of their own, suggesting that he and the other homeless people there are motivated and relishing the fact that they have agency again.

- He talks about the abandoned shipyard and the "scrap" materials they could use to build "crude shelters". Although this language highlights how basic these constructions would be, Jackson states they would be a "big improvement" over the Central Registry, suggesting that the conditions there were truly shocking.

3. You might have said that the tone is personal. Jackson uses the first person ("I", "we", "us") throughout, which helps to establish a connection with the reader. Jackson is also open about his "suffering", using a more informal style at times, like when he says started to "find a way to get away from the whole thing".

Don't worry if you've talked about a different tone to the one above — just make sure that you've used evidence from the text to support your view.

4. You could have said that the extract begins with Jackson alone at the Central Registry for "single homeless men", but ends with him sat around a "camp fire" speaking with other "shanty dwellers" where they give Hooverville its name. This difference interests the reader by emphasising how friendships and a community have developed.

5. All your points should use relevant examples from lines 19-28, use relevant terminology and comment on the effects of the language used to describe the attempted evictions. Here are some things you could have mentioned:
   - The writer describes the authorities as a "regiment of uniformed officers", which makes them sound like an advancing army. The description of how they "swooped" on the homeless people also compares the officials to birds of prey, attacking their victims. These descriptions depict the homeless people as helpless victims who are hunted down and attacked, which makes the eviction seem brutal and heartless.
   - Jackson says how they "returned and rebuilt" after the authorities burned their "shacks". This language and use of alliteration highlights their resilience and shows that the attempted evictions are doomed to failure in the face of their collective determination.
   - Jackson mostly uses long sentences in the extract, so his use of short sentences at the end of this paragraph stands out, for example: "This time we did not rebuild, but dug in, indeed." The blunt, conclusive nature of these sentences emphasises further that the attempted evictions are unlikely to succeed because the community are so determined.

Pages 29-30: Exercise B — London Labour and the London Poor

1. You could have talked about how Mayhew describes the topic as "one of the most important" — using a superlative engages the reader, and emphasises the significance of the topic and the text as a whole. Or you could have mentioned that the writer ends the paragraph with the bold statement that "the young vagrant is the budding criminal". This shocking statement might intrigue the reader and encourage them to question why the writer has formed this opinion.

2. You might have said that you think the intended audience is the upper-classes, or those in power, then explained why you think this. For example:
   - His writing seems to be biased towards those in power. His sole "informant" was in charge of a union and he presents those in power as being kind and "sympathising" with the vagrants.
   - Mayhew uses quite complex language and sentence forms, which suggests that he expects his audience to be well educated, and therefore probably upper-class.

3. All your points should use relevant examples from lines 14-26, use relevant terminology and comment on the effects of the language used to describe the young people. Here are some things you could have mentioned:
   - The writer describes the young people as surprisingly fit and healthy with descriptive phrases, such as "physically stout, healthy lads". His description of them as "certainly not emaciated" creates a sense of irony, as the reader might expect the boys to be unhealthy or starving because they are vagrants.

Answers

- The writer uses several verbs to present young people as being aimless, such as "wandering", "loiter" and "searching". This suggests the purposelessness of the young people and acts as evidence for the writer's damning description of them as "the idle" because they seem uninterested in finding any real purpose.
- The young people are described by a pair of superlatives ("most dishonest" and "most difficult") which state that they are the worst type of criminal, thus creating a strongly negative impression of them. This impression is highlighted further by the writer's use of intensifiers in the phrases "very stubborn" and "great delight", which reinforces the negative depiction of the boys.

Page 31: Exercise C — Comparing Texts

1. Make sure you've compared the writers' views about those in power in detail, using examples from the extract to support your argument. Here are some things you could mention:
   - Mayhew presents the authorities as sympathetic, as the union "guardians" offer the homeless "refuge". His language here could be seen to evoke a sense of parental care and responsibility. However, Jackson's attitude seems to directly challenge this. He sees the authorities as aggressive, detailing how officers "swooped down" upon them with "cans of kerosene". The verb "swooped" suggests their arrival was abrupt and savage, likening the authorities to a bird of prey targeting the homeless.
   - Both present the authorities as being unable to control the homeless. Mayhew states that vagrants are a "difficult class to govern", whilst Jackson says that the residents of the Hooverville "paid no attention to the notices" and "rebuilt" the shanty town. Mayhew's language encourages the reader to sympathise with those in power, as the vagrants are presented as criminal and rebellious. Jackson's language, however, makes the actions of the "shanty dwellers" seem inspirational and empowering, as they're acting out of resilience and desperation.

2. You should have summarised the differences between how the writers represent homeless people, using quotations and inferences to support your points. Here are some things you could have mentioned:
   - Jackson presents the homeless as "willing workers" and industrious, noting that "within 30 days the shanty town had grown to near 100 shacks". Jackson's inclusion of this statistic emphasises the Hooverville residents' determination and impressive work-ethic. In contrast, Mayhew portrays homeless people as "idle" and having an "aversion to continuous labour". This negative language condemns the vagrants' attitudes, and encourages the reader to see them as lazy and have little sympathy for them.
   - Jackson presents the homeless as people who have been unlucky and want to better their situation. It is implied that they are only homeless because it was "such a time as this", the time being the Great Depression and the hardship it brought. However, Mayhew describes vagrants as lads who had been "reared to a life of vagrancy" and had "generally run away". He suggests that these boys are "vagrants" simply because that is who they are, rather than through unfortunate circumstances, like in Extract A.

Section Six — Getting Away From It All

Pages 32-34: Exercise A — A Lady's Life in the Rocky Mountains

1. a) You should have given an example of hyperbole with an explanation of its effect. For example, you could have said that Bird's description of how "The barns are bursting with fullness" uses hyperbole to exaggerate how full the barns are with harvested food: this suggests that the harvest is exceptionally abundant.

b) You should have talked about how Bird creates a negative impression of Sacramento. Here are some things you could have mentioned:
   - Bird uses intensifiers and negative adjectives to create a highly unappealing impression of Sacramento Valley, describing it as "Very uninviting" and "very repulsive". This pair of adjectival phrases makes Bird's unfavourable impression clear. By putting this description immediately after her positive depiction of bountiful farmland in the "Golden State", Bird uses juxtaposition to reinforce how unpleasant the Sacramento Valley is compared to other places.
   - Bird uses statistics ("103 degrees in the shade") to emphasise how hot the city of Sacramento is. This gives a clear, factual point of reference for the reader and emphasises that the city is uninhabitable due to the insufferable warmth.

2. You should have talked about how Bird suggests she's moving away from civilisation, supporting your ideas with evidence from the extract. Here are some things you could have mentioned:
   - Bird says that when they began their ascent of the Sierras, the mountains had already been in sight "for many miles". This shows that Bird had already travelled a long distance.
   - After repeatedly using the word "dusty" to describe San Francisco in the second paragraph, Bird says that the "dusty fertility was all left behind" in the third paragraph. This uses the reader's knowledge of her previous description to emphasise how far she's travelled.
   - Bird uses a lot of comparatives, noting that the ridges were becoming "longer", the ravines "deeper", and the pines "thicker and larger". The use of comparatives to describe the natural scenery in this way emphasises how the landscape is becoming wilder as her journey progresses.

3. You should have agreed or disagreed with the statement, and used relevant examples to support and explain your view.
   If you agreed with the statement, you could have mentioned:
   - Language such as "a dream of beauty" and "exquisite purity" clearly shows Bird's amazement at the landscape around her. By having this language at both the beginning and end of the extract, it presents Bird's amazement as the overriding feeling of the extract, and therefore the overall tone is arguably one of enthusiasm.
   - Bird seems to notice a great deal about her surroundings — even during parts of the journey she doesn't enjoy. On her route out of San Francisco, she comments on everything from the barns "bursting with fullness" to "superb "red" horses". These vivid descriptions suggest that she has a level of enthusiasm about everything she encounters.
   If you disagreed, you could have mentioned:
   - Although Bird shows a great enthusiasm for nature, her description of San Francisco makes up a large part of the extract. As she presents the city in a very realistic, maybe even pessimistic way, it is hard to say that the overall tone of the extract is one of enthusiasm.
   - Bird chooses to "pass hastily over the early part of the journey". This suggests that she feels that some stages of the journey are more mundane and not as worthy of recounting as others, which makes her enthusiasm questionable.

4. All your points should use relevant examples from lines 1-8, use relevant terminology and comment on the effects of the language used to describe the landscape. Here are some things you could have mentioned:
   - Bird uses listing to describe the landscape, noting everything from the "snow-splotched mountains" and "pine-hung lake", to several different types of tree. This listing emphasises the variety and beauty of the landscape.
   - Bird uses regal language, such as "silver", "crystalline" and "snow-crowned" to describe the landscape. These adjectives imply she finds it both majestic and precious.
   - Bird uses factual language, informing the reader that the lake is up to "1,700 feet deep" and "lies at a height of 6,000 feet". This is a common feature of travel writing, and aids the reader in gaining a comprehensive idea of the landscape.

Answers

5. All your points should use relevant examples from lines 9-19, use relevant terminology and comment on the effects of the language used to describe San Francisco. Here are some things you could have mentioned:
    *   Bird uses onomatopoeia to describe the "clang" of the city. This evokes the sound of metal crashing together, like pots and pans, suggesting the city is noisy and disruptive. By stating that it's a "weariness" to even think about the "clang" of the city, Bird suggests that she found San Francisco draining and overpowering.
    *   Bird uses a list of nouns, coupled with the verbs "piled" and "heaped", to describe the different foods she saw in the city. This list creates a sense of how overwhelmingly busy the city is, and gives an impression of the vast volume of produce passing through.
    *   Bird chooses to capitalise the word "RAINLESSNESS". Stressing this word suggests that she is frustrated by the city's weather, and when combined with the repetition of the adjective "dusty" ("dusty vineyards", "dusty melons", "dusty earth"), it emphasises the impression of the city as dry, dirty and uncomfortable.

Pages 35-36: Exercise B — The Exmoor Files

1. You could have talked about how the word "moat" makes the reader think of a barrier, suggesting that the house is remote, difficult to reach, and that its isolation would deter people from attempting to get to the house. You could have mentioned how it suggests that the house is quite grand and imposing, as moats are normally associated with castles.
2. You should have identified the style of the extract as personal or autobiographical, and then talked about the methods Jones uses to achieve this style. Here are some things you could have mentioned:
    *   Jones writes in the first person throughout. In fact, most sentences in the second paragraph begin with "I" followed by a verb ("I bump across a cattle grid"). This instantly makes the text more personal and autobiographical, as she is recounting her own thoughts and experiences.
    *   Jones writes in the present tense, making her actions and thoughts more immediate, and making the reader feel like they are experiencing everything at the same time as her. This heightens the reader's sense of having a personal relationship with the writer.
    *   Jones uses a mixture of simple and complex sentences. This helps to give the extract a similar flow and rhythm to conversation, which helps build a friendly, personal tone.
    *   Jones includes descriptions of different aspects of her life, such as her "cats" and her "BMW convertible". She also includes her opinions and thoughts, sometimes tagging "I think" onto her statements. This all contributes to giving the reader an impression of her life, personality and thought processes, which is key to autobiographical writing.
3. All your points should use relevant examples from lines 18-33, use relevant terminology and comment on the effects of the language used to describe the farm. Here are some things you could have mentioned:
    *   The repetition of "my" emphasises Jones's delight at every detail of the farm. The short sentence "My gate." reflects her realisation that the farm belongs to her, which builds to a sense of excitement when it dawns on her that she owns the trees too: "('My oak trees!')", "('My sycamores!')". The use of exclamations and parenthesis here suggests her growing internal excitement about owning the farm.
    *   Later in the extract, Jones's description of the farm becomes more negative. The short sentence "Everything is pretty gloomy." suggests an abrupt loss of enthusiasm, which is reinforced by an exaggerated negative description of the fields, which are "so green" that they "hurt" her eyes.
    *   Jones creates a strong contrast between her initial, positive impression of the farm during the summer ("charming and olde worlde") and the reality of the farmhouse now, which looks like it is "about to fall down". The adjective "olde worlde" suggests that her previous impression was rose-tinted and fanciful, whereas her later descriptions emphasise the practical reality of living at the old, decaying farm.

Page 37: Exercise C — Comparing Texts

1. You should have compared the purpose of both texts.
    If you think they are similar, you could have mentioned:
    *   Both texts are intended to describe the writer's surroundings to the reader and give their personal opinions on the places by using a first-person narrator. Bird uses detailed descriptions to praise the places she loves, such as the "dream of beauty" Lake Tahoe, and condemn places she dislikes, such as the "very repulsive" city of Sacramento. Similarly, Jones describes her delight and disappointment about her farm in Exmoor, focusing on small details such the "taste" of the air which brings the description to life.
    If you think they are different, you could have mentioned:
    *   Jones's book was written to entertain, so she uses comedic devices to make the text engaging, such as the humorous aside describing the estate agent as "about 12". Jones also focuses more heavily than Bird on her shifting thoughts and emotions. These entertain the reader and make them emotionally invested in her story, from her excitement at "('My sycamores!')" to her realisation that the property is "about to fall down".
    *   Bird's text is written to inform the reader about her travels. She focuses on describing what she has seen, such as the "boundless harvest fields", and includes facts about her surroundings (Lake Tahoe "lies at a height of 6,000 feet") to inform her reader. This information is presented more impartially than that in Jones's book, with Bird making only a few, brief references to the effects of her surroundings on her own emotions.
2. You should have used relevant examples from both extracts to compare the writers' different perspectives and feelings about being away from the city. Here are some things you could have mentioned:
    *   Bird seems to be happier in the countryside than Jones. She uses vivid language to juxtapose the "musical ring" of the countryside with the "clang" of the city. This contrasting sensory language emphasises how she finds the countryside more calming than the city. On the other hand, while Jones seems excited by the prospect of moving away, she is frustrated by the reality of her decision. She seems to find the countryside uncomfortable and unfamiliar. She describes how the cobbles made her "teeter", suggesting that she is uncertain of the terrain.
    *   Through the language they use to describe nature at the start of each extract, Bird and Jones suggest that being away from the city offers peace, at least at first. Bird builds an idyllic picture of nature, claiming to have "found a dream of beauty" at Lake Tahoe. Her descriptions of "snow-crowned summits" and a "crystalline atmosphere" suggests that nature can be both powerful and peaceful. Jones seems equally amazed by the countryside at first. She comments on its energy and power ("following the raging, bubbling River Exe"), but also its isolation, excited at the prospect that the lane to her home is "the next best thing to a moat".
    *   Whilst Jones's excitement about being away from the city fades, Bird's doesn't. Towards the end of the extract, Jones becomes frustrated. Her attitude changes and she describes the surroundings that she first saw as vibrant as "pretty gloomy" by the end. The final paragraph of Bird's extract, however, reminds the reader of her passion for nature. Having left the "weariness" of San Francisco, she describes the "exquisite purity" of the Sierras, seemingly pleased to have left the "last traces" of civilisation behind.
    *   Jones presents the journey away from the city as difficult, whereas Bird makes little reference to the journey itself. Jones describes the journey to Exmoor as "fraught". Words like "bump" and the onomatopoeic "crunch" are used to describe her driving and make the journey sound physically uncomfortable. On the other hand, Bird's more general descriptions make her journey seem smoother. She simply describes "driving to the Oakland ferry" and "crossing the bay", but doesn't provide further details, preferring to "pass hastily" over the journey. Even in the "rocky and gravelly" Sierras, where there are "broken ridges and deep ravines", Bird merely says that they "ascended", suggesting the journey is not her focus.

Answers

Section Seven — Food for Thought

Pages 38-40: Exercise A —
Partnership for a Healthier America

1. a) You should have picked out two examples from the correct part of the extract which show how Obama appeals to her audience, then explained the effect each example has. For example:
   - By opening the speech with "I want to thank all of you", Obama uses direct address. This creates a connection with the audience, grabs their attention and involves them in the speech she is about to deliver from the very start. You could add that this is flattering and makes the audience feel good about their involvement so far, which encourages them to continue listening.
   - Obama makes a joke about how "fast" the campaign has grown by saying how it feels like her "child". This humour sets an informal and chatty tone. Obama speaks as she would with friends, which engages the audience.

   b) You could have talked about how these words emphasise the different elements of the anniversary celebrations, and serve as a memorable and concise message which the audience can take away. This is aided by the fact that all three words begin with the letter 'c'.

2. You should have talked about how Obama says that lots of places are starting to take healthy eating seriously and promote healthy lifestyles. She says that this is a big change from what things were like five years ago.

3. You should have talked about how Obama structured the speech to appeal to her audience. Here are some things you could have mentioned:
   - At the start of the speech, Obama introduces the theme of the anniversary as "Celebrate, Challenge, Champion". She returns to these three ideas in turn, expanding upon each one. This structure ensures a full understanding of the theme and gives the speech a clear focus.
   - Each of the speech's three main ideas has a different tone, which helps to emphasise the three-part structure of the speech. The "Celebrate" section features an up-beat tone, before the "Challenge" part is introduced by a shift to a more realistic tone. Then, during the "Champion" section, Obama builds an inspirational tone. This helps to highlight the three different focuses in the speech.
   - Obama introduces new ideas with discourse markers such as "I want to start off", "Just think" and "that brings me to the "Champion" part". These discourse markers serve as 'signposts' for the audience, guiding them through the speech as it progresses. This also helps to build the speech's conversational tone, creating the sense that Obama is walking the audience through her ideas and objectives.

4. You could have said that you don't agree with the statement because Obama tells her audience she wants to be "very clear" that she "has no intention of slowing down" on the issue of healthy eating. She says "I have a rest-of-my-life horizon" for the issue, which shows that she has a long-term ambition for the campaign and doesn't want to lose momentum. However, this strong, almost defensive language implies that Obama has faced such criticism before. She frequently refers to "our kids" and her role as "a parent", which suggests that this is a matter of importance to her outside of politics. Her use of emotive language when referring to children as "our future" further strengthens the idea that she is speaking as a concerned parent, or citizen, rather than simply as First Lady.

Don't worry if you have a different opinion to the one above — just make sure that you've used evidence from the text to support your view.

5. All your points should use relevant examples from lines 15-25, use relevant terminology and comment on the effects of the language used to describe children's health. Here are some things you could have mentioned:
   - Obama uses a list of three examples to bluntly describe the multiple challenges facing children's health. By focusing on the issues faced by "doctors", "Businesses" and "Parents", she emphasises the widespread nature of the problem.

   - Emotive language, such as "incredibly fragile" and "daunting", is used to highlight the severity of problems in children's health. This language attaches emotional weight to children's health, making the audience want to support Obama's cause in order to help children.
   - Obama uses statistics, telling her audience that "one in three kids" is overweight or obese and that health care will cost "$350 billion a year by 2018". This shocks the audience by highlighting the scale of the problem facing children's health with factual evidence.

Pages 41-42: Exercise B —
The Idle Thoughts of an Idle Fellow

1. You should have talked about the effect of humour in the extract, using an example to support your point. For example:
   - It keeps the reader entertained. For example, Jerome tells the reader that his father called him "Colly wobbles" at the same time he asked his father what "dyspepsia" means. As 'collywobbles' means stomach pain and dyspepsia means 'indigestion', Jerome creates a sense of irony which is humorous and encourages the reader to continue.
   - It helps to make the text more relatable. Jerome often uses humour when referring to situations the reader may be familiar with. He refers to "individuals" who talk to children "vaguely — about sixpences". This humorous generalisation would help readers of the time recall such men, and therefore relate to Jerome's point of view.

2. a) You should have talked about how the adjectives "sour" and "starchy" suggest that the individuals are unpleasant, bitter and stiff. Jerome's use of food-related adjectives mirrors the semantic field of the text, which helps to convey his idea and adds to the light-hearted tone.

   b) You might have said that Jerome uses exclamations to emphasise the joy and excitement of eating after a long walk. They imply that he is shouting or stressing his points, as if he is proclaiming them directly to the reader. The use of the second person ("How your eyes will glisten") also emphasises and exaggerates the emotion of the exclamations.

3. All your points should use relevant examples from lines 32-38, use relevant terminology and comment on the effects of the language used to describe cooking. Here are some things you could have mentioned:
   - Jerome uses an extended metaphor to compare the cooking ritual to a religious one, referencing a "temple", "vestal flame"and "high-priest". This comparison highlights his passion for food by implying that cooking is sacred. In the context of the 19th century, when religion played a more prominent role in society, this metaphor would have been even more effective.
   - Jerome uses vivid adjectives ("chief", "roaring", "mighty") to build a sense of power surrounding cooking. He then says that the cook is God's "prophet", which implies that he is holy, all-powerful and to be respected.
   - Jerome ends the extract with a list of three imperatives: "eat, drink and be merry". In this sequence of verbs, eating and drinking lead directly to being "merry", which reinforces the pleasure that cooking can bring to people.

Page 43: Exercise C — Comparing Texts

1. You should have compared the style and tone of both extracts. Here are some things you could have mentioned:
   - Both Obama and Jerome adopt a friendly, chatty tone. Obama uses informal language, referring to "plenty of folks" and a "drive-thru". This helps to build a connection with her audience by creating the impression that she is speaking like she would with her friends. Jerome uses humour to create a light-hearted tone, like in his description of individuals who look "as if they lived on vinegar and Epsom salt". His light-hearted humour keeps the reader engaged with the text.

Answers

- Both Jerome and Obama build a personal tone. Jerome does this by telling stories from his childhood, such as how people called him "Colly wobbles". Obama uses emotive language to share her feelings as a mother, saying that "as parents, there is nothing we would not do for them — nothing". The repetition of "nothing" emphasises her point and heightens the personal emotion of the statement.
- Obama infuses her speech with statistics ("we still spend nearly $200 billion a year on obesity-related health care") and technical language ("special interests lobbying"). This suggests that her speech is intended to be more factual in style. Jerome wishes to share his thoughts and opinions, as suggested by the book's title "Idle Thoughts of an Idle Fellow". He writes about his past and his views in a much more anecdotal and autobiographical style than Obama.

2. You should have used relevant examples from both extracts to make comparisons between the ways the writers present their perspectives on eating. Here are some things you could have mentioned:
   - Jerome glorifies the experience of eating. By using a metaphor to compare cooking to a religious ritual and saying that "the stomach is the real seat of happiness in this world", he suggests that eating is one of the most important and enjoyable aspects of life. Obama, however, does very little to celebrate eating. She focuses on "eating right" rather than worshipping food, and praises how the culture around eating has changed. This implies that she welcomes a shift away from the adoring way that Jerome presents eating.
   - Jerome uses sensory language to present eating as enticing. He describes the "glistening eyes", "steaming dishes" and "sigh of content" at meal times, which helps to persuade the reader to share his view that food provides "much gratification". Obama refers to food in a very matter-of-fact way, simply giving examples of the foods involved in her campaign. She doesn't attempt to build a tempting atmosphere around the "fresh produce and whole grains", perhaps echoing the campaign's message about adopting a different attitude to food.
   - Jerome suggests that food has power over people. He says that "a good dinner brings out all the softer side of a man", before using vivid description and humour to explain how "the gloomy and morose become jovial and chatty". However, Obama emphasises that people have power over food, and that they have the ability to change their behaviour around eating. She praises companies for "rewarding employees for eating right" and convenience stores for "selling fruits and vegetables".

Section Eight — On the Money

Pages 44-46: Exercise A — Advice to a Young Man

1. You should have ticked boxes A, C, D and G only.
2. You could have said that writing about his own experiences provides evidence for his argument — by referencing the fact that he studied for his "degree" at the university and then was given a position of authority there, the reader is led to believe that Berens is a knowledgeable voice. It suggests that his words can be depended upon and believed.
3. a) You should have said that Berens feels that the cost of going to university isn't that high and that it would be difficult to find anywhere cheaper to live in England. However, he believes that students should budget whilst at university in order to avoid getting into debt. He seems to believe that debt only really affects students who get carried away and make unnecessary purchases.
   b) You might have said that Berens's viewpoint may be biased. The writer states that he studied at Oxford, then "became a Fellow of Oriel". It could be that by holding a position of influence within the university he would be keen to defend it, which could have led to bias within his writing.
   If you think that Berens's viewpoint isn't biased, that's fine — just make sure that you can back up your argument with evidence from the extract.
4. You should have talked about the techniques used to create an authoritative tone, and stated whether or not you find it effective. Here are some things you could have mentioned:
   - Berens implies that he is speaking from experience, stating that he was "at Christ Church" himself. This makes the reader trust his voice more and helps to create the sense that he is an authority on the subject.

- Berens uses direct address, speaking clearly to the reader — "I trust that you are resolutely determined". This builds a sense of confidence and commands attention. This use of the second person continues in commands like "be on your guard", where imperatives help create an authoritative tone.
- This tone is effective because it adheres to the purpose of the text, which is to advise. Berens creates a clear and convincing voice, which the reader is likely to find trustworthy and believable.
- This tone makes Berens appear like a parent or teacher. This builds a sense of fear and power, which would probably be effective in encouraging students to follow his advice.

Feel free to say that you didn't find Berens's tone effective — just make sure you've used evidence from the text to support your view.

5. All your points should use relevant examples from lines 26-35, use relevant terminology and comment on the effects of the language used to describe debt. Here are some things you could have mentioned:
   - Berens uses extremely negative language to describe how debt produces "evil and misery of every description". The nouns "evil" and "misery" create a strong sense of terror. This is emphasised by the phrase "of every description", which shows how comprehensive Berens believes the negative consequences of debt to be.
   - Berens uses hyperbolic language when he describes debt as "positive dishonesty". By saying that a person in debt is effectively lying about the possessions they own, Berens presents debt as something immoral and unjustifiable.
   - When discussing debt, Berens asks the reader "is not that something approaching to robbery?" This rhetorical question encourages the reader to consider debt as criminal. This makes them more inclined to then agree with Berens's condemnation of debt.

Pages 47-48: Exercise B — How to Keep a Budget While at Uni

1. a) You might have said that the extract has a friendly, conversational tone.
   b) You should have identified features that the writer has used to achieve the tone you talked about in part a). Here are some things you could have mentioned:
   - Colloquial language is frequently used to create a friendly tone. The writer offers advice on how to "snap up a few bargains" and account for expenses that are "clumped together". This informal language makes it sound more like a conversation between friends.
   - The writer uses direct address throughout the extract, telling the reader that "you can learn to keep a budget". This builds a more personal tone and creates the effect that the writer is reaching out to the reader individually.
   - The writer also makes use of humour, joking that paying full price for a book isn't worth it, especially if it "goes untouched until exam time". This creates a sense of friendliness, implying that the writer understands the reader and isn't judgemental.
   c) You could have said that you think it would appeal to the intended audience (people at or about to go to university). You should then have explained why you think this. For example:
   - The writer uses a mixture of formal and colloquial language throughout the text. University students would perhaps find this style of writing more appealing than other audiences because it mirrors the way that they speak as young but educated people.
   - University students are generally known for socialising more frequently than other groups within society. Therefore, by mentioning going out "for lunch or dinner" and discounts at "pubs and bars", the writer has used examples which reflect the lives of the intended audience. This makes their advice more appealing and relevant.

Answers

2. All your points should use relevant examples from lines 3-15, use relevant terminology and comment on the effects of the language used to describe budgeting. Here are some things you could have mentioned:
   - Short subheadings that summarise paragraphs (e.g. "Set a budget" and "Prepare meals at home") simplify the advice into brief points. This helps to make budgeting sound manageable and logical.
   - Short clear sentences (e.g. "This is a student budgeting staple.") and simple language make budgeting feel relatively straightforward. These simple sentences, paired with a conversational style, make a complex financial discussion accessible to younger readers who might not have much experience with managing money.
   - Statistics, such as "a coffee each weekday over four weeks can cost more than $70!", highlight the importance of budgeting by giving factual evidence of how it can save students money. The use of an exclamation here suggests that the statistic is meant to shock and impress the reader, which makes budgeting seem like an important skill.

Page 49: Exercise C — Comparing Texts

1. A — Both   D — Extract B
   B — Both   E — Extract B
   C — Extract A   F — Extract A
2. You should have compared the differences between the writers' attitudes to spending money at university, using relevant examples and terminology to support your points. Here are some things you could have mentioned:
   - The Good Universities Guide writer frames their argument in a more positive way than Berens. They begin their extract with a reassuring statement, telling the reader that "If you think being a student means being poor, think again!" The use of direct address and an exclamation mark helps to emphasise this positivity. The opening of Berens's letter, however, warns against being "hampered" by debt, stating that there will be "little" money "for the indulgence of pleasure".
   - Berens uses fear-inducing language, such as "entangled in debts", to evoke a sense of panic and constriction. He exaggerates his points, saying that budgeting requires "a great deal of care and attention". The Good Universities Guide writer has a different attitude, saying that budgeting only takes a "little self-restraint". By saying that budgeting "doesn't mean always saying 'no'", and using adverbs such as "only" and "even", the writer suggests that following this advice is achievable and not restrictive.
   - Both writers offer really clear advice, but how they give this advice reflects their different attitudes. Berens's writing is filled with strict commands, for example "do not buy anything merely because it hits your fancy", which provide the reader with rules they should follow. Whilst Berens uses commands to restrict the reader, The Good Universities Guide writer uses commands positively, encouraging the reader to adopt certain habits ("Learn to 'shop smart'"). Their advice is presented through solutions and tips, such as "you might do some research". Verbs such as "might" and "may" also suggest that the reader has a choice, and present the writer's attitudes in a less severe way.
   - Berens's attitude appears to have a stronger moral focus, as he mentions crime and implies that the reader should have a "proper feeling and a nice sense of honour". He encourages them to think about how their actions will affect others. In contrast, the Good Universities Guide writer seems to present their argument more as an aid to help students avoid personal difficulty and deprivation. It focuses on helping the students themselves rather than presenting a wider moral lesson like Berens's text.

Section Nine — Heading to the Capital

Pages 50-52: Exercise A — London Characters

1. a) You should have picked out the simile: "he feels as one of many cogs in one of the many wheels of an incessantly wearing, tearing, grinding, system of machinery". You could have talked about how the simile gives the impression that living in London is exhausting and unpleasant, or that a person loses their identity in London. Phrases such as "one of many cogs" and "a system of machinery" suggest that a person becomes a small piece of something larger and mechanical, losing their individuality.
   b) You should have talked about the other ways languages is used to give you the impression you talked about in part b) and given examples from the text. Here are some things you could have mentioned:
      - The writer uses antithesis to show how living in London reduces a person's worth. This can be seen when the writer says "However great a customer before he feels a small customer now". The contrast of "great" and "small" emphasises how a person feels important outside the city, but insignificant within it.
      - The writer contrasts the nouns "Mr. Brown" and "No. XXI" to show the transformation that occurs when living in London. It suggests that a person goes from being an individual with a personal identity to simply one of a number of people living in the city.
      - The writer uses a list of three to say that customs aren't as "strange, strong, or inexorable" anywhere else as they are in London. This emphasises how the ways of London are overpowering and relentless.
2. You should have said that the tone in the third paragraph becomes more positive towards London and explained how the writer creates this effect. For example:
   - In the first two paragraphs, the writer uses negative language, such as "a small customer", to describe how London makes a person feel, but in the third paragraph the writer uses more upbeat phrases, such as "brightens up the wits", to show the positive effects London can have.
   - The first two paragraphs don't consider the positive aspects of London, but the third emphasises the opportunities the city can offer by saying it has "new images, new people, and new sensations". The repetition of "new" emphasises the exciting and fresh things the city has to offer.
   - In the first paragraph, the writer uses short clauses to describe how a London tradesman "serves, takes your money, and turns away". The verbs are all about the tradesman, making them seem more interested in the money than the customer. However, in the third paragraph, such clauses become longer. Phrases such as "the buying and the selling, the counting and the weighing" have a regularity to them which creates a pleasant rhythm, and makes the acts of buying and selling seem more equal.
3. a) You should have summarised any two differences between city life and country life that the writer gives in the extract. Answers might include:
      - In the city, tradesmen don't talk that much, whereas in the country talking is part of how the selling is done.
      - There are a lot more people coming and going in the city than there are in the country.
      - People in the city walk for the sake of getting from place to place, whereas people in the country are happy to wander without purpose.
   b) You should have talked about whether you think the writer prefers city life or country life and given an explanation of why you think this. For example:
      - You could have said that you think the writer prefers country life over city life because they say there are "Many other things" that "make our new Londoner feel smaller". The use of "Many other" creates the impression that there are almost too many reasons why city life can make someone feel small to cover.
      - You could have said that you think the writer prefers city life over country life because of the way the extract has been structured. Although the writer begins with negative points, they then shift to focus on the positives. As the positives come after the negatives, it means that the writer has left the reader with a positive impression of London.

Answers

4. All your points should use relevant examples from lines 13-26, use relevant terminology and comment on the effects of the language used to describe the people of London. Here are some things you could have mentioned:
    *   The writer uses a metaphor to describe the people on the streets of London as a "living stream", which makes the people sound like one body of water. This suggests that the crowds are large, but also that the people in them are anonymous and have lost all sense of their individuality in the fast pace of London life.
    *   The writer juxtaposes the single-minded attitude of Londoners with the newcomer's bewilderment at this behaviour. The writer describes the "determination" of Londoners, who "resolutely" move towards their destination. In contrast, the new arrival in the city is "jostled" by those moving past him, which shows his unfamiliarity with this pace of life. This emphasises how particular this purposeful way of life is to those who live in London, and the strangeness of this attitude to those who have newly arrived in the city.
    *   The writer uses a simile to describe how Londoners "live as in a mill" due to the constant noise generated by the city. This suggests that the people of London are like factory workers, accustomed to working tirelessly in unpleasant and noisy conditions without complaint. By describing this as a Londoner's "normal state of nature", the writer ironically suggests that Londoners lead unnatural lives.

Pages 53-54: Exercise B — Londoners

1. You could have talked about how the "half-opened doors" reflect the barrier Taylor has to overcome to really belong in London. Describing the doors as only "half-opened" suggests Taylor gets a tantalising peek into London life, but is stopped from fully taking part. If you felt differently, you might have said that they imply there are many opportunities in London, making it seem like an inviting city with lots of places to explore.
2. You should have talked about how the text has been structured to interest you as a reader. Here are some things you could have mentioned:
    *   Taylor uses a chronological structure, which gives his account a story-like quality. However, even when he's not living in London, he keeps referring back to the city. This constant calling back emphasises how the city is always on Taylor's mind, and makes the reader support him in his desire to return there because it seems so strong.
    *   There is a sudden shift in tone at the start of the second paragraph when Taylor states "My visa expired." This short sentence is jarring after the long descriptions in the first paragraph, creating tension and emphasising the impact this had on his life. The change in tone leaves the reader wondering if Taylor will return to London. This question is considered by Taylor himself, who feels "a mixture of love, ambivalence and loathing" towards London. His inner conflict highlights the very different ways he feels about the city and encourages the reader to find out why he might have such strong contrasting emotions.
    *   Taylor shifts the focus between paragraphs for dramatic effect. At the end of the penultimate paragraph, Taylor says he felt "defiant, bold" and "victorious" upon returning to London, but then the final paragraph starts with: "I didn't dare call myself a Londoner". Including this at the end of the extract shows that Taylor is still unsure about his place in London. The shifts in focus throughout the extract highlight the complexity of Taylor's feelings towards London.
3. All your points should use relevant examples from lines 10-15, use relevant terminology and comment on the effects of the language used to describe life in a village. Here are some things you could have mentioned:
    *   Taylor uses sensory imagery to describe life in a village. He describes walking "under dark skies", and hearing "the rustle of trees". By appealing to multiple senses, Taylor creates the impression that nature surrounds people and therefore features prominently in village life.
    *   Taylor describes life in a village as having a "consistent tempo". The adjective "consistent" suggests that life in a village is routine and uneventful. Taylor implies that this "tempo" can be comforting, describing how life "made sense" when it followed the regular rhythms of the village.

*   The use of a list of three nouns ("Growth, family, death"), without any other words to describe or elaborate on the ideas, emphasises the simplicity of life in a village, and suggests that life in a village follows a straightforward, conventional pattern.

Page 55: Exercise C — Comparing Texts

1. A — Extract A   D — Extract A
    B — Extract B   E — Both
    C — Extract B
2. You should have compared the similarities between the writers' feelings and perspectives about London, using examples and terminology to support your points. Here are some things you could have mentioned:
    *   Both writers feel that London is an unfriendly place. The writer of Extract A achieves this by describing the "indifference" of the tradesmen, and using adjectives like "small" and "little" to describe how this attitude makes a new Londoner feel insignificant and unwelcome. Taylor makes the city seem unfriendly by using personification to describe London as something that "disgorges people every day". This creates the image of London spitting out its inhabitants and suggests that the city isn't a caring place.
    *   Both writers think London is a place where people can be better than they were before. The writer of Extract A praises the pace of the city at the end of the extract. They say that the city "brightens up the wits" and can "stretch" the mind, suggesting that London's testing pace can make a person more mentally agile. Taylor describes how returning to London made him feel more empowered. He does this by listing a triplet of positive adjectives "defiant, bold, victorious". This creates the sense that returning to London has renewed him after time away from the city.
    *   Both writers believe London is full of people, but in different ways. The writer of Extract A uses a metaphor to describe people travelling the streets of London as a "living stream". This makes it seem like the people move as one body, as though there's no sense of personal identity. Taylor also describes the city as full of people, but lists the many nationalities of the people who live there. These lists not only emphasise the number of people living in the city, but also the diversity of these people. Doing this highlights how London is a multicultural city, compared to Extract A, which suggests that the people of London are all the same.
    *   Both writers view London as a fast-paced city, but describe the effect of this speed in different ways. The writer in Extract A lists the negative adjectives "wearing, tearing, grinding" to describe the exhaustion someone feels when they move to London due to the "incessantly" fast pace of the city. The listing of these adjectives emphasises how draining and relentless life in London is. Similarly, Taylor uses the phrase "London is propulsion" to suggest that speed and energy is what defines the city. However, whereas this pace seems to hurt London's inhabitants in Extract A, Taylor says the city "rewards those people who push forward" and describes himself as someone who can "push on", showing he feels like he benefits from the fast pace of London life.

Section Ten — Fashionable Thoughts

Pages 56-58: Exercise A — Environmental Costs of Fast Fashion

1. You should have ticked boxes C, E, G and H only.
2. You could have explained that clothing manufacturers are financially motivated, so they are more likely to prioritise methods that will help them sell their products. Perry says that consumers need to be tempted by "constant newness" to keep buying clothes, and that in order to "deliver frequent new collections", manufacturers focus on "speed and low costs", meaning that "environmental corners are more likely to be cut".

Answers

3. You should have said to what extent you agree with the statement, using examples to support your view.
    If you agreed with the statement, you could have mentioned:
    - Perry suggests that people who buy fast fashion contribute to the environmental impact of it by providing demand for the companies who then cut "environmental corners". She suggests that people find it a hassle to maintain their clothes for longer, saying it is "more convenient to buy new than have an item repaired". The word "convenient" suggests that people make a choice to buy fast fashion simply because it's easier, which makes it sound like Perry doesn't sympathise with them.
    - Perry ends the second section with the fact that "three-quarters of Britons throw away unwanted clothing, rather than donating or recycling it." This creates the impression that people who buy fast fashion don't really think about the environmental impact, especially because they could easily donate or recycle their clothes.

    If you disagreed, you could have mentioned:
    - Perry appears to sympathise with people who buy fast fashion because of their busy lifestyles. She describes people as "time-poor", and suggests that their buying habits contribute to an "unintended consequence" of fast fashion. The words "poor" and "unintended" suggest that people are not wholly at fault for the effects of fast fashion.
    - Perry dedicates a whole section of the text to how people can improve their shopping habits to tackle the problem of fast fashion. This creates the impression that she knows how hard it is to be an environmentally conscious shopper, sympathises with this difficulty and wants to help people.

    You could partly agree with the statement, saying that Perry suggests that people who buy fast fashion contribute to environmental problems, but that they are also the victim of manufacturers' marketing techniques and retailers who "convince" people that their clothes are "no longer fashionable".

4. a) You should have talked about how the writer uses language to inform and given examples from the text. Here are some things you could have mentioned:
    - The writer uses listing to describe the effect fast fashion has on the environment. She states that its consequences include "negative environmental impact, water pollution, the use of toxic chemicals and increasing levels of textile waste". This listing emphasises the many ways fast fashion harms the environment and gives the reader an informative summary.
    - The writer uses lots of assured statements, such as "it is particularly bad for the environment", to present information in a confident way. This makes her points feel more convincing, and presents her as an authoritative individual who knows what she's talking about.

    b) You should have talked about how the text has been structured to inform readers. Here are some things you could have mentioned:
    - Splitting the text into sections with subheadings helps to inform the reader. Each of the three sections talks about a different part of the environmental impact of fast fashion: the role of clothing manufacturers, the role of shoppers and finally what shoppers can do to decrease this impact. This creates a clear and logical structure that helps the reader access the information more easily.
    - The writer first informs the reader of the problems of fast fashion before informing them of the things they can do to combat these problems. By structuring the text in this way, the writer explains first why people should take action, allowing them to clearly understand the impact of the solutions as they read about them.

5. All your points should use relevant examples from lines 9-18, use relevant terminology and comment on the effects of the language used to describe the fashion industry. Here are some things you could have mentioned:
    - The adjectives used to describe the products fashion companies use present them as volatile and bad for the environment. Words like "toxic" and "hazardous" indicate the dangerous nature of the chemicals used, and aren't normally adjectives someone would associate with clothing. This may shock readers and emphasise the negative environmental impacts of fast fashion.

- The writer uses language to show the damage caused by the fashion industry. She says that "Textile dyeing is the second largest polluter of clean water globally". The use of "second largest" and "globally" emphasises the widespread damage fast fashion causes to the environment.
- The writer uses the verbs "tempt" and "convince" to make the fashion industry seem calculated and persuasive. This casts the fashion industry in a sinister light and suggests they are manipulating their customers in order to sell them things they don't need.

Pages 59-60: Exercise B — Caper-Sauce

1. You should have talked about how Fern uses different language to describe young and middle-aged people's opinions about fashion, and explained the effect it has.
    Here are some things you could have mentioned:
    - Fern uses different adjectives to describe each group's interest in fashion. Young people are described as "clamorous" for change, while middle-aged people are described as having an "abated" interest in new clothes. These adjectives highlight the stark contrast in enthusiasm between the groups, as "clamorous" makes young people seem loud in their desire for fashion, while "abated" suggests a lessened interest from middle-aged people.
    - Fern uses sarcasm to comically highlight the different attitudes that both groups have towards fashion. The exclamation "perish the thought of not wearing either!" emphasises the ridiculous nature of young people forcing themselves into painful new clothes out of vanity. In contrast, the statement "appearances as the gods please" stress how little those in middle age care about wearing fashionable clothes.

2. You should have talked about how Fern presents merchants and parents, using evidence to support your answer. Here are some things you could have mentioned:
    - Fern uses unflattering adjectives to describe merchants. She refers to them as "heartless" and says that they "care little" for what clothes their customers choose. This makes them appear ambivalent to the interests of their customers and suggests that they are more focused on their own interests, such as making money off people.
    - Fern uses the oxymoron "happy slaves" to suggest that parents are content to be taken advantage of because of their love for their babies. You could have said that this humorously inverts the usual parent-child relationship, because the parents are almost being controlled by their babies instead of making more sensible "economical decisions". This emphasises how strong a parent's desire is to provide nice things for their children.

3. All your points should use relevant examples from lines 1-15, use relevant terminology and comment on the effects of the language used to describe new and old clothes. Here are some things you could have mentioned:
    - New clothes are described by verbs like "squeeze", "strangle" and "pinch" to suggest that they can be painful. This highlights how young people are willing to endure pain for the sake of new fashion trends.
    - In contrast, old clothes are described with the words "easy" and "Comfort" to suggest that they are pleasant to wear, unlike the painful new clothes.
    - The writer describes the cyclical relationship between new and old clothes: middle-aged people purchase new clothes but they only "feel easy" to wear once they become old and "threadbare", which in turn prompts the realisation that they need to buy new clothes again. The use of hyperbolic descriptions to describe this cycle ("fretting intrusion", "treacherous", "horrifies") is humorous, emphasising the comic nature of the relationship between new and old clothes.

Answers

Page 61: Exercise C — Comparing Texts

1. You should have compared how consumers are presented in each extract. Here are some things you could have mentioned:
   - Both writers present critical attitudes towards consumers, but for different reasons. In Extract A, Perry says that those who buy fast fashion often do so out of convenience (buying new is "cheaper and more convenient" than repairing items), suggesting they're doing it mainly out of laziness. In Extract B, Fern uses a series of rhetorical questions to criticise parents for buying unnecessary clothes for their baby ("Why don't they cross right over and travel home out of the way of temptation?").
   - Despite their criticisms, both writers present consumers as being manipulated into buying goods. In Extract A, Perry says that people are more "time-poor" and easily manipulated by marketing tricks such as "seasonal sales", while in Extract B Fern refers to parents as "happy slaves", suggesting that they are not the ones in control of their buying choices. Both writers therefore present consumers as being easily manipulated.

2. You should have compared the different attitudes of both writers to fashion, using examples and terminology to support your points. Here are some things you could have mentioned:
   - The writers have different attitudes to fashion, which are shown through the different focuses of each text. Perry focuses on the "negative environmental impact" of fast fashion and what consumers can do to "reduce the environmental cost", reflecting her attitude that this is a problem that needs addressing. In contrast, Fern presents more of a social commentary, talking about how people "at different stages of existence" interact with fashion, which suggests she has a less of an issue-focused attitude towards it.
   - The tone of each extract reflects the writers' different attitudes. Extract A has a more serious tone, using factual phrases like "organic cotton still requires high amounts of water" to convey Perry's message about environmental damage. This tone emphasises the devastating impact of fast fashion and highlights her more serious attitude towards fashion in general. Extract B has a more chatty tone. Informal phrases like "squeaky soles" and "spick-and-span" feature sibilance, which creates a light mood that reflects Fern's more relaxed and light-hearted attitude to fashion.
   - The writer of Extract A presents a negative attitude to the low cost of fashion, whereas the writer of Extract B worries about the high financial cost of fashion. Perry says the "pressure to reduce the cost" of fashion is damaging as these pressures lead to manufacturers cutting "environmental corners". This shows that Perry believes low-cost fashion harms the environment. In contrast, Fern thinks too much money is spent on clothing: she uses the negative verb "sunk" to describe how money is spent on new clothes. The verb "sunk" evokes the image of a shipwreck, suggesting that Fern sees the use of money in this way as a loss or waste.
   - The writers structure their texts in different ways to express their different attitudes to fashion. Perry structures her article logically with an intriguing introduction, subheadings that split up the text and make it easier to read, and a clear conclusion which instructs the reader on what they can do to minimise their environmental impact. This logical structure shows that Perry wants to inform the audience about the issues with fast fashion, which suggests how important it is to her that others have a clear understanding of these issues too. In contrast, Fern structures Extract B through a series of loosely linked, humorous reflections on how different people approach fashion. This entertaining structure reflects her attitude that fashion is frequently ridiculous and can be a source of comedy.

Section Eleven — Intrepid Explorers

Pages 62-64: Exercise A — Travels in West Africa

1. You should have identified what you think the purpose of the extract is and then explained your reasoning. For example:
   - The purpose of the extract is to inform readers about West African swamps. Kingsley uses detailed descriptions, such as the description of the mangrove roots, to educate readers about the swamps in depth.

- The purpose of the extract is to provide an entertaining insight into the writer's travels. Kingsley infuses the extract with humour, such as the image of the mangroves "displaying their ankles" in a shocking way, or the idea of an "at home" for "crocodiles and mangrove flies".

2. You should have said that Kingsley thinks that canoeing through the mangrove swamps is fascinating but dangerous. She enjoys how the swamps offer her freedom to explore, but she is also very aware of how this beauty can be deadly, as highlighted through the crocodiles.

3. You could have talked about how in each paragraph of the extract, Kingsley focuses on the mangrove swamps in more detail. In the first paragraph, she describes them from a distance ("They look most respectable"), before discussing her own experience "among the swamps in a small dug-out canoe" in the second. The extract then ends with a very detailed explanation of how a "network of roots" develops into land. This structure maintains the reader's engagement and interest by gradually increasing their involvement, and slowly giving additional detail to their mental picture of the mangrove swamps.

If you didn't make this point, don't worry — as long as you've supported any structural points you made with evidence from the text and explained how they interest you as a reader, that's the most important thing.

4. a) You might have said that this makes the reader think Kingsley is modest, because she describes her abilities as "ordinary" even though she was a confident Victorian woman who did things that weren't expected of women at the time, or you might have said that it tells the reader that Kingsley has a sense of humour because she is able to make fun of herself.

   b) You should have said whether you think Kingsley's account is authentic or not, and supported your opinion with evidence from the text. Here are some things you could have mentioned:
   - Kingsley draws upon her own personal experience to convey authenticity to the reader. She uses sensory descriptions, mentioning sight ("you do not see"), touch ("grasp the mud"), and smell ("the fearful stench"). This language gives the impression that Kingsley felt and saw everything she talks about first hand, and makes her account seem believable to the reader.
   - The level of detail in Kingsley's writing indicates that she is faithfully describing the swamps. For example, she specifies that mangrove roots spread out "some two feet above water-level" and that "flood tide" is the time when crocodiles tend to be awake. This specificity suggests that Kingsley has carefully checked the details she provides, which reassures the reader that her account is authentic.

Remember — if you don't think a simple 'yes' or 'no' answer is suitable then you can say so, as long as you explain why you think this and support your view with evidence from the text.

5. All your points should use relevant examples from lines 25-39, use relevant terminology and comment on the effects of the language used to describe the mangroves. Here are some things you could have mentioned:
   - Kingsley uses personification to encourage the reader to engage with the text on a more emotional level. Describing how the first mangroves "struggle" for life emphasises how difficult their life is and makes the growth of the mangroves seem like a real, human endeavour instead of just a natural process. This encourages the reader to empathise with the mangroves.
   - The use of a simile to describe the mangroves "like a net gripped in the mud" paints a clear image for the reader. The familiar image of the net in this description allows the reader to easily visualise the tangle of mangrove roots in the mud. The use of the verb "gripped" in this simile also suggests how firmly the mangroves are rooted in the mud.
   - The use of an extended metaphor presents the growth of the mangroves as a dramatic fight against nature. The first mangroves are described as "pioneer mangrove heroes" who have "laid down their lives" in order to allow future mangroves to "colonise" the swamp. This makes the reader invested in their struggle and results in a satisfying conclusion when the mangroves successfully conquer the mud.

Answers

Pages 65-66: Exercise B — Wildest Dreams

1. You should have talked about how the tone changes throughout the first paragraph. Here are some things you could have mentioned:
    *   The tone at the start of the paragraph is happy and enthusiastic. The writer is "full of self-congratulation" after finding the "perfect spot" to camp.
    *   The tone becomes uncertain at the start of the second sentence with the word "Yet", before becoming more negative with the word "raided".
    *   The tone becomes humorous at the end of the paragraph when it is revealed that the "culprits" were just "mountain goats". This humour is reinforced by the description of the family "banging picnic plates" to chase the goats away.

2. You should have said how you think the writer feels about the tourist industry and used evidence from the text to explain your views. Here are some things you could have mentioned:
    *   She does not seem to approve of mass market package holidays. She describes them as being "peddled" by "most tour operators". This suggests that she views them as unoriginal rather than unique like camping. The verb "peddled" implies that they are blindly offered to anyone and that tour operators just want to make money, which emphasises McAuslan's negative opinion to the reader.
    *   She seems to think that many holidays in Oman are too expensive. She describes "holiday accommodation" prices as "exorbitant", which highlights this opinion. She also talks about how the government are "pumping billions into luxury developments", which suggests she dislikes the way the wealthy seem to be targeted instead of the government making holidays accessible to everyone.
    *   She describes the shopping mall that will resemble London's Westfield shopping centre as a "replica", emphasising how it's merely a copy rather than something original or interesting. This contrasts with her earlier descriptions of Oman's "natural beauty", emphasising her negative feelings about the focus of the tourist industry.

3. All your points should use relevant examples from lines 27-43, use relevant terminology and comment on the effects of the language used to describe the desert. Here are some things you could have mentioned:
    *   The writer uses supernatural language to describe the desert. Phrases such as "an eerie beauty" and "a ghostly splendour" give the impression that it is an incredible and almost otherworldly sight. Using these spooky adjectives with nouns associated with radiance emphasises this strangeness.
    *   The writer uses factual language to give the reader a more detailed image of the desert. The reader is told statistics like "about 82%" of the country is desert and that some dunes "tower nearly 100 metres high." This use of language emphasises that the desert is a real, tangible place despite its supernatural connotations.
    *   The writer uses harsh language to describe how dangerous the desert can be despite its beauty. She refers to the "knife-sharp edges" of the dunes, which makes the reader think of violence and peril.

    You could have said how combining language of beauty and danger creates a contrast which shows how complicated and awe-inspiring the desert is.

Page 67: Exercise C — Comparing Texts

1. You should have compared the style and tone of each extract and written about the effect they have on the reader.
    Here are some things you could have mentioned:
    *   The writers address their audience in different ways. Extract A directly addresses the reader in the second person as "you", as if they are there with Kingsley. The use of direct address creates a conversational tone and helps to immerse the reader in the landscape that Kingsley describes. In contrast, extract B does not directly address the reader. Instead, the use of the first person gives the text an anecdotal style, which means that the reader observes what happens on McAuslan's holiday from an outside perspective and can enjoy reading about the writer's experiences without necessarily imagining that they are with her in the desert.
    *   Both extracts use an entertaining yet informative style and tone. Kingsley describes the growth of the mangroves in detail, but with informal and unscientific language such as "the thing's done". Similarly, McAuslan blends statistics about the desert with informal terms such as "budge" and "plumped for". This creates a relaxed tone in both extracts, which helps to keep the reader entertained and makes the information in the text easier to process.

2. You should have compared the writers' similar perspectives and feelings about travel, using relevant examples and terminology to support your points. Here are some things you could have mentioned:
    *   Both writers have a practical approach to travel. They both travel to potentially dangerous locations: Kingsley to the mangrove swamps where "several natives" have died after being attacked by crocodiles, and McAuslan to a desert where you could "perish within hours" if you weren't well-prepared. However, both proceed with caution. This shows how they want to get the most exciting experience possible without taking too many risks in the process.
    *   Both writers have positive feelings about where they've travelled. Kingsley seems to admire the mangrove swamps, describing the "pioneer mangroves" as "heroes". McAuslan shows a more introspective admiration, saying how although they have "beauty", the sand dunes make her think about her own "mortality". The way the desert prompts her to think about life and death reinforces how moving the sight is.
    *   Both writers present their respective perspectives clearly and effectively to their readers, using amusing personal anecdotes to engage the reader and make them feel involved in their travels. For example, Kingsley sarcastically mocks her own "retiring nature" and McAuslan discusses her son's "apocalyptic Instagram shots". This encourages the readers to connect with the writers of each extract and makes the writers' feelings and perspectives easier to understand.

Section Twelve — Learning the Lingo

Pages 68-70: Exercise A —
The Mastery of Languages

1. You could have talked about how this technique illustrates the quantity and variety of reasons that have been put forward to explain how children learn languages so successfully. Listing these "reasons" emphasises the amount of research Prendergast has carried out. It shows he's familiar with all the "proposed" theories and finds them "unsatisfactory". This informs the reader of his expertise and might make them trust his view more.

2. You should have identified the device as a simile, and then explained its meaning and effect. Here are some things you could have mentioned:
    *   It means that the very first pieces of information a child receives become etched in their mind, and that even though new information and ideas will be introduced, the initial ones will never be removed.
    *   Prendergast uses this device to sum up this "reason" in a more useful and interesting way than the others he has previously listed. This perhaps suggests that he gives this reason more credit than others in the list, or feels like it is the most complex and needs further explanation.
    *   By referring to a "sheet of paper" and "scribblings" in the comparison, Prendergast is using language from the same semantic field as the overall topic (study and education). This helps to emphasise the point he is making.

3. You should have talked about how Prendergast believes that repetition isn't only useful for introducing sentences to children, but that it's also key to maintaining and broadening their use of sentences too. He states that children pick up new vocabulary by using words they don't know alongside ones they do, and that they learn to pronounce words by watching and listening to them being spoken.

Answers

4. You should have said that it means children are good at learning language because they do so in the most natural way, and that when we reach adulthood we stop doing this. "Light" implies that this method is the most enlightening and serves to guide us, and the word "beacon" suggests that the light is glaringly bold and bright, as though to attract attention. This emphasises how he deems adults foolish to have "ignored" it.

5. You should have identified the intended audience of the extract as educated adults, especially those learning a language or interested in language acquisition, and explained how the writer's language suits this audience. Here are some things you could have mentioned:
   - The writer uses complex language throughout the extract. His references to "physiological function" and even "the principles of grammar" elevate the tone and level of the text. This sophisticated language would attract and engage the writer's educated audience, and also helps to make his argument appear more reliable.
   - The writer uses figurative language to make his ideas more accessible. For example, the extended metaphor about "trains of thought" expresses his ideas about sentences in a more visual way. This would not only ensure that his audience understands his argument more clearly, but that they are entertained and remain engaged by the text.
   - In the final paragraph, the writer adopts the first person plural by saying that "we have ignored that beacon". Although he presents himself as a person of expertise throughout the extract, the use of the first person shows how he puts himself on the same level as the reader. This would engage the audience, as it builds a connection.

6. All your points should use relevant examples from lines 20-28, use relevant terminology and comment on the effects of the language used to describe sentences. Here are some things you could have mentioned:
   - Prendergast builds an extended metaphor around the concept of "trains of thought". This is effective, as he uses a concept the reader is most likely already familiar with to explain his idea that learning sentences is the key to learning language. It's also memorable and engaging, and so appeals to the reader whilst making his argument clearer.
   - By stating that sentences are "the rails", he suggests that sentences are the fundamental elements by which language learning progresses. This also implies that learning by this method follows an established and direct path. He says that "each language" establishes a "separate line of rails", suggesting that through this method, children are able to learn multiple languages at once, without any confusion.
   - Prendergast also uses alliteration, such as in "swiftly, smoothly, and without the slightest deviation". The sibilance in this phrase emphasises the smoothness of the process and increases the pace, which highlights the speed and efficiency of learning a language by repeating sentences. Alliteration also reflects his point about learning by the "imitation and repetition" of sounds.

Pages 71-72: Exercise B — Acting French

1. You should have talked about the effect of Coates referencing childhood in the extract. Here are some things you could have mentioned:
   - Coates often mentions childhood in relation to adulthood. For example, he describes how "childlike amazement" is often "dulled away by adult things", and that he's heard that it's easier for children to learn a second language. He therefore presents childhood as a time when people are more curious and able to learn things more easily. Including this in an article about his adult learning experiences creates a contrast, and highlights how difficult he finds learning a new language.

- Coates considers how his own childhood has shaped him, drawing parallels between his background and its consequences in his life now. For example, he says that he sometimes regrets not having an adult passport until he was 37, but that travelling now allows him to be "young again". However, when talking about learning languages, he says that he spoke to a woman who had spoken multiple languages since childhood because everyone in her "world" did so. Unlike with his passport, where he sees a positive to not having had one for so long, he doesn't present a positive to not learning multiple languages as a child — he sees no benefit to having missed out on this experience.

2. All your points should use relevant examples from lines 11-19, use relevant terminology and comment on the effects of the language used to describe learning French. Here are some things you could have mentioned:
   - Coates's use of a long sentence containing a sequence of verbs ("watched films", "tried to read", "listened to") stresses the quantity and variety of things he does to learn French. In addition, he has to do "four hours" of class work and "four hours" of homework. This makes the process of learning French seem very time-consuming and difficult as it requires intense practice and commitment.
   - The idea of the writer's mouth feeling "alien" when he speaks English demonstrates how immersed in learning French he became. He is so engrossed in French that speaking his native language has become unnatural to him.
   - The short sentence "Acquiring a second language is hard." succinctly communicates the writer's feelings about language learning. The direct, blunt nature of this sentence draws the reader's attention and so stresses to the reader the difficulty of learning French.

3. All your points should use relevant examples from lines 20-32, use relevant terminology and comment on the effects of the language used to describe the writer's classmates. Here are some things you could have mentioned:
   - Coates seems to be impressed by his classmates, such as his description of how they could quickly memorise a poem in a language they didn't understand. He claims that this flair for study comes from a "culture of scholastic achievement", and that rather than this being "acquired yesterday", it had been "ingrained" into the students. This suggests that it is common amongst his classmates, and is something deeply embedded in their nature or personality.
   - Coates appears to find his classmates intimidating. He tells the reader: "They had something over me", which shows that he feels at a disadvantage. Coates repeats "They knew" three times to suggest the various ways in which he feels his classmates are academically superior to him. His fixation on all the things his classmates knew — and which he did not know — shows why he found them intimidating.
   - Coates marks his classmates out as being different to him, calling them "fiercer" and "younger". The comparative adjective "fiercer" not only shows difference, but also implies a sense of aggression — this highlights how Coates feels intimidated by them. He also refers to his classmates with the pronouns "they" and "them", which creates a clear divide between him and the rest of the class.

Page 73: Exercise C — Comparing Texts

1. You should have compared how each writer presents ideas about youth. Here are some things you could have mentioned:
   - Both writers present youth as having benefits over adulthood by depicting young people as better than adults at learning languages. Prendergast describes the ease with which languages can be learnt in youth as a "feat" which surpasses even "men of the best education". Similarly, Coates writes that people say it is "easier for children" to learn languages. They therefore both present youth as a time where people are able to learn new things more easily.

Answers

- Both extracts use comparatives to present youth positively. Prendergast uses a long list that includes comparatives such as "greater power of concentration", "greater quickness and retentiveness of memory" and "better adapted" to describe how children are well-suited to learning languages. Similarly, Coates describes how his classmates are both "younger" and "fiercer" than him. By using comparatives to express why young people are better at language learning than adults, the writers suggest being young has advantages over being older.

2. You should have compared the writers' different perspectives and feelings about learning languages in detail, using examples and terminology to support your points. Here are some things you could have mentioned:
   - Both writers have different attitudes to learning languages through immersive methods. Prendergast believes that immersion in the language, "observing and mimicking" those who speak it, is the most natural way to learn, and that by intensively studying language we have "deviated from the right course". Coates seems to disagree. He undertook a course where pupils were immersed in the language, yet found that "scholastic achievers" who had a "culture" of study found it much easier to learn, suggesting that he believes studying greatly aids the process.
   - Both writers understand that there's a difference between how adults and children learn languages, but to different levels. Coates says that he's been told it's easier for a child to learn a second language, but isn't sure whether it's due to "biology" or because "adults have so much more to learn". Prendergast is more certain, saying that children succeed because they approach the task in a more natural way. He adds that when adults start to learn in a similar way, they should have "every confidence of success". Prendergast's more assured and detailed explanation reflects his more scientific approach to the topic.
   - Coates presents his attitudes through his own experiences, using a more personal tone, whereas Prendergast uses a research-based approach. Extract B is written in the first person ("I have not been many places"), and is packed with anecdotes and observations. In contrast, Prendergast presents his attitudes in a more detached way. He walks the reader through his evidence and reasoning, using words like "when" and "hence" to guide them. Prendergast's thorough and detailed writing effectively communicates his attitudes, yet Coates's personal, more informal style is perhaps more engaging to the reader.
   - Prendergast uses more figurative language than Coates. For example, Prendergast refers to immersive learning as a "beacon", sentences as "the rails" of language acquisition, and a child's brain as a "sheet of paper" — this helps the reader to understand the abstract ideas he presents. Coates, however, relies more on his journalistic style to clearly, yet engagingly, express his ideas to the reader, such as when he relays his conversation about learning languages at the end of the extract. Prendergast's use of figurative language to clarify his argument reflects his desire to inform and enlighten people about his method of learning, whereas Coates's style reflects the more autobiographical and introspective tone of his article.
   - McAuslan is only on a week long break and so takes a more methodical approach to her travel. She has a roughly planned itinerary ("Our plan was to take in three locations over a week"), with every family member choosing a location to visit. In contrast, Kingsley's travels feel much more like an exploration than a holiday. Kingsley takes the time to describe her current location in great detail throughout the whole extract, which emphasises how she is free to explore without a plan or a time limit.

Section Thirteen — Practice Paper

1. You should have shaded boxes B, F, G and H only.
2. You should have summarised the differences between how the writers learn new skills, using quotations and inferences to support your points. Here are some things you could have mentioned:
   - Whereas learning new skills is a private experience for Temple, Mount enjoys learning as part of a collective experience. Temple is a self-taught artist, who experiments with sketching alone "to amuse" herself. In contrast, Mount attends a "crash course" in oil painting with "eight friendly ladies", taught by a teacher.

- The writers learn new skills in different settings. Temple enjoys learning things "out of doors", painting the "scenery" and flowers she sees around her. In contrast, Mount learns to paint in a "huge, well-lit room" in a pub by studying a still-life of an apple that the teacher has arranged.
- The writers use different methods to learn new skills. Temple prefers learning from the world around her rather than the instruction of others; she advocates for learning from "God's book of Nature" rather than being taught by "bound books". Mount, meanwhile, chooses to learn new skills from established authorities on the subject, like his teacher, "artist Dani Humberstone", and the example of famous artists such as "Caravaggio".

3. All your points should use relevant examples from lines 20-32, use relevant terminology and comment on the effects of the language used to describe the flowers. Here are some things you could have mentioned:
   - Temple uses a simile to describe how the "bright, golden-green leaves" of the flowers "shone like stars". By comparing the flowers to stars, Temple suggests the flowers are so bright that it's as if they're physically giving off light. She reinforces this imagery by renaming the butterworts "heath-stars" to reflect their beauty. By renaming the flowers, Temple elevates them above their status as mere "bog-flowers". This suggests the depth of her admiration for them.
   - Temple uses a strong statement to describe her desire to paint the flowers. She states: "I could not help trying to paint them, there and then." This clear statement shows that the beauty of the flowers strongly compelled her to paint them. The final phrase "there and then" adds a sense of urgency to the compulsion she feels, further emphasising the enchanting beauty of the flowers.
   - Temple uses vivid language to help the reader visualise the appearance of the flowers. She describes their "graceful, slender flower-stems" which spring in "curves", and the "brilliant colouring" of their petals. These detailed descriptions create a clear image of what the flowers looked like for the reader.

4. You should have used relevant examples from both sources to compare the writers' different perspectives and feelings about creating art. Here are some things you could have mentioned:
   - Mount finds it easy to enjoy creating art, whereas for Temple these feelings are more complicated. Mount recognises that his artwork is poor, but states that he "didn't mind the failure", suggesting that the quality of his art does not affect his enjoyment of the activity. Temple, on the other hand, initially finds creating art frustrating: she uses emotive language to describe her "despair" and "vexation and sorrow" at the "grievous failure" of her landscape drawings. Over time, however, she accepts that her art "was not to be despised", which suggests that she eventually learns to see the value in painting even when it isn't perfect.
   - Temple finds it important for others to appreciate the art she creates: the fact that her paintings bring others "a great deal of pleasure" gives value to her art "on that plea alone", suggesting that she views her art positively when it is received positively by others. In contrast, Mount places no particular importance on other people's opinion of his art: he is unconcerned with the teacher addressing the "shortcomings" of his painting. Instead, he uses a metaphor to describe how he is "transported to a different universe" when painting, which suggests that he is only concerned with the escape from daily life creating art gives him.
   - The writers describe different advantages to creating art, and express these benefits with very different tones. Temple uses a thoughtful, reflective tone to describe how creating art has taught her "many a lesson of patience" due to the process of trial and error inherent in learning to draw. Mount, meanwhile, uses a flippant, humorous tone to express how he finds "trying — and failing" to create art a welcome distraction from his "cursed phone".

ENCAWN42